A Forest of Wormwood

Also by Niels Sparre Nokkentved
Desert Wings: Controversy in the Idaho Desert
WSU Press, 2001

A Forest of Wormwood

Sagebrush, Water and Idaho's Twin Falls Canal Company

By
Niels Sparre Nokkentved

Printed in the United States of America by

Caxton Printers, Ltd.
Caldwell, Idaho

Library of Congress Control Number: 2008906779
    Nokkentved, Niels Sparre, 1947 –
    Index included
    Black and white photos, maps
    Idaho history—Water development and irrigation in Idaho—
Western agriculture—Western History—Water rights—Water law

ISBN 978-1-60702-252-7

Front cover:
Surveyor John Hayes plants a white flag in the spot in the sagebrush that would become the corner of Shoshone and Main streets
in downtown Twin Falls. Courtesy of Robert K. Maddox Jr.

Back cover:
"Map of Oregon, Washington, Idaho and part of Montana" 1860
by S. Augustus Mitchell Jr., used with permission of the Idaho
State Historical Society.

Photos not credited are by the author.

Contents:

Dedicated to those who died while working on the Twin Falls Canal Company system.

1913 - James King: Died of pneumonia after falling in canal.

1929 - Charlie O'Toole: Killed in a dredger accident.

1930 - Harley Gambrel: Killed in a ditch cave-in.

1930 - W. M. McConnel: Killed in a radial gate accident.

1930 - Dutch Aston: Killed by falling rock at Milner Dam.

1933 - WPA Employee Killed in a tunnel accident.

1936 - Albert Wavra: Killed in a tunnel accident.

1936 - Fred Greason: Died of pneumonia contracted in tunnel.

1936 - Johnny Denardis: Died of pneumonia contracted in tunnel.

1936 - Jack Sorenson: Killed by a blasting explosion.

1938 - Garland Curly: Killed in a tunnel accident.

1942 - Benton Reece: Killed in a tunnel accident.

1970 - Paul Palmer: Drowned in main canal.

1971 - Auborn Orr: Killed in a tractor accident.

1999 - Mark Briere: Killed in a Magnacide H accident.

Foreword

By John W. Keys

Every once in a rare while, an opportunity comes along to read and learn about an old friend and close colleague. Such was the case when Niels Nokkentved asked me to review *A Forest of Wormwood*, a story of southern Idaho's Twin Falls Canal Company, its history and the issues it faces today.

Idaho is blessed with one of the best irrigation systems in the world. Its mix of Carey Act, Bureau of Reclamation, and private projects serve about six million acres of land with water for the agriculture that is the mainstay of its economy.

Managing these projects and their intricate water supplies is a Herculean effort, accomplished admirably by the canal companies, irrigation districts, and private associations that have been established under Idaho Law. Nowhere is this effort more effective than in the Snake River Basin of Idaho.

During my tenure with the Bureau of Reclamation, it was my good fortune to work with districts and companies throughout the state. One of the leaders that I came to know well and respect very much was the Twin Falls Canal Company – its Boards of Directors, its managers, and its dedication to its water users.

A Forest of Wormwood sets the stage for irrigation in Idaho and the Snake River Basin; it follows the early development of the Twin Falls Canal Company; it gives intimate details on the normal and the not-so-normal work that it takes to keep the water running and to manage the Canal Company; and it covers the continuing challenges to the Canal Company as the system ages, water needs escalate, and the water supply fluctuates with the runoff of the basin.

John Keys
Moab, Utah, December 2007
(John Keys worked with the Bureau of Reclamation for almost forty years, serving as engineer, Pacific Northwest director, and as Commissioner from 2001 through April 15, 2006. Keys, 66, died May 30, 2008, in a small plane crash in Canyonlands National Park.)

Author's Note:

I want to thank canal company officials for their support and for reading this manuscript for factual accuracy--particularly Joe Webster, for his invaluable help with historic photos. I also want to thank Jennifer Sandmann of Burley for her generous and patient editing and Paul Smith for his encouraging words, without which this project would not have been completed.

A note about the sources for this book: The opinions and conclusions in this book are my own--based on more than twelve years of reporting on the Twin Falls Canal Company and water issues in Idaho—supported by research from a variety of sources. Those quoted directly are noted in the text. The rest are listed in the back of the book. I want to acknowledge two notable sources. For details on dam and canal construction I relied on "A History of the Twin Falls Canal Company," by J. Howard Moon, July 1985. For details on the Carey Act, I used "The History of Development and Current Status of the Carey Act in Idaho," a report by Mikel H. Williams published in March 1970 by the Idaho Department of Reclamation, now known as the Department of Water Resources. And for the details of the Swan Falls case, I relied on the archives at the Twin Falls *Times-News*.

Before moving on, I need to introduce and explain a few key terms that may be unfamiliar but are essential to understanding water issues.

Acre-foot: A measure of volume. It is enough water to cover an acre with one foot of water and equals about 326,000 gallons, or about the amount needed to supply an average family of four for one year.

Cubic foot per second: A measure of flow. It is the amount of water passing a point in a stream each second. One cubic foot holds about seven and a half gallons, thus one cubic foot per second equals about four hundred fifty gallons per minute. One cubic foot per second—cfs—over twenty-four hours adds up to two acre-feet.

Miner's inch: A unit of flow. Fifty miner's inches make up one cubic foot per second. An irrigation rule of thumb says that it takes one cubic foot to irrigate eighty acres, and thus fifty miner's inches for eighty acres means each acre gets five-eighths of an inch, which for many irrigation companies is the contracted amount delivered to each farmer.

Preface

More than 200 years before Captains Meriwether Lewis and William Clark ventured into the interior Northwest in the early 1800s, Spanish settlers were farming irrigated fields in the Southwest. As early as 1598 they established settlements in what are now New Mexico and Arizona. Here they found conditions similar to their own arid country, where without irrigation even basic agriculture was impossible. And they encountered a society of American Indians who had long ago learned to divert seasonal streams into simple ditches to move water to their crops nearby. The Spanish settlers added their own irrigation practices to build irrigation systems that took advantage of gravity, diverting water into ditches that followed the contours of the landscape. Like the Indians, the Spanish knew that settlements required a dependable food source, and a dependable food source required irrigation. Survival depended on the construction of irrigation systems and careful allocation of water, and the settlers often built ditches even before churches or houses.

These irrigation systems and the communal structure that grew up around them have their roots in the Moorish culture, brought to Spain by Muslims in the Middle Ages. The southwestern term "acequia" comes from the original Arabic name—"as-saquiya"—and can refer to the actual irrigation channel, the association of members organized around it, or both, writer Stanley Crawford says in "Mayor Domo: Chronicles of an Acequia in Northern New Mexico." In these remote settlements, the acequia served at once as a system to maintain the ditches and control the distribution of water, and as the local government. The acequias formed the foundations of the earliest form of European government in what was to become the United States.

The acequia was governed by a commission of landowners known as "parciantes" or shareholders, who were assessed work or money for water, according to the amount of land irrigated or number of shares they owned. Each year, the parciantes elected a person, known as the "mayor domo," to manage the day-to-day operation and maintenance of the ditch and to control the allocation of water. "As mayor domo you become the pump, the heart that moves the vital fluid down the artery to the little plots of land of each of the cells, the parciantes," Crawford writes.

For the community, then as today, the ditch formed a source of common prosperity, and each community member depended on the cooperation of the other members to keep the water flowing and equitably distributed. All members of the community participated in the construction and maintenance of the system and helped with repairs. As a bonus, water in some systems also turned water wheels that ran mills. About sixty acequias operated in New Mexico by 1700, another hundred by 1800, and three hundred more by 1900. Some of them still function more than four hundred years later.

Irrigation has a history almost as long as human civilization. Archeological evidence shows that inhabitants of the Tigris and Euphrates valley, in what now is Iraq, practiced irrigation as early as 5000 B.C. Irrigation still depends on the availability of fresh water that can be pumped from the ground or diverted from streams. Around the world, fresh water is scarce. A mere 3 percent of the water on the earth's surface is fresh water. Two-thirds of that is ice bound up in glaciers, snowfields, ground ice and permafrost. Groundwater makes up nearly one-third. The tiny bit remaining is surface water in lakes and rivers.

In the United States today, the largest consumer of fresh water is irrigated agriculture, mostly in the arid West. West of about the 100th meridian, the average annual rainfall drops below 20 inches, which is the minimum needed to support most kinds of agriculture. This arid region stretches west to the Cascade Mountains in Oregon and Washington and the Sierra Nevada range in California. Prevailing westerly winds blowing in from the Pacific Ocean drop most of the moisture they carry as they climb the coastal mountains. As the winds come down the eastern side of the mountains, warming and expanding, they soak up moisture. That makes for lots of hot, dry summer days with clear blue skies. But with the minimal rainfall, farmers can't raise a dependable crop without irrigation.

Early settlers in the West struggled individually or in small groups to build irrigation diversions, mostly of brush and dirt, to supply the ditches for their fields. Most farms were small and on lands close to their water sources. These small irrigation systems, however, meant agriculture and the beginnings of settlement. In some places, ample water was unreachable at the bottom of deep canyons. Large rivers—the Colorado, Sacramento, Columbia and Snake—flowed through the arid West. But the raging spring floods that poured out of the interior mountains made anything more than temporary structures impossible for individual farmers. The resources—money, engineering and construction expertise—to build dams sufficient to wrest the water from the wild rivers were beyond the reach of the early settlers. Taming nature's obstacles would require massive amounts of money.

Late in the nineteenth century hydraulic engineers with their transits and levels did more to shape the American West than early trappers or cowboys with six-guns. They harnessed the rivers, and they laid out and built the irrigation systems that brought water and settlers to vast tracts of new agricultural lands. Trappers blazed the trails that brought pioneers, and prospectors established some of the first towns. But large-scale irrigation projects, some financed by eastern bankers and many by the federal government, brought permanent settlements to the arid West.

Irrigation in the West today is largely associated with federal water projects, built and operated by the U.S. Bureau of Reclamation. About 61 million acres of farmland—nearly 11 percent of the 546 million acres farmed in this country—depend on irrigation. Federal reclamation projects account for irrigation water on 11 million acres. The most common crop grown on irrigated lands is forage to feed cows, and most of the irrigation water is provided with federal aid. Federal officials run the water systems. Political connections are more important than community, and irrigators don't have to depend on each other to keep the water flowing.

But that is not true everywhere.

There are notable exceptions where private money developed irrigation systems, much like the ancient acequias that continue to thrive. In south-central Idaho cooperation created an irrigation system and a community that has thrived for more than a century, operating on principles very similar to the acequias of the Southwest.

This book is about the Twin Falls Canal Company, its history and the issues it faces today. It's about the people who built it and who continue to make their living with the water it supplies, and about how the irrigation system has shaped their lives. It's about the adventurous souls who explored the region and those who settled in southern Idaho and learned to make the best of the arid topography. It's about the ancient geologic forces and the river that shaped the landscape and made large-scale irrigation possible, and about the ancient inhabitants who were cleared from the land like the sagebrush to make room for European settlement.

And it's about the problems caused by a century of irrigation. It's about the conflicts that arose among competing users of a fickle water supply and the laws that grew up to resolve those conflicts. And it's about the uncertainty that the future holds for a nineteenth century canal company in the twenty-first century, and about the threats presented by the growing and competing demands for water as the population continues to grow in Idaho and the rest of the arid West.

This book is intended as a portrait of a place that illustrates the dependence of human societies everywhere on the availability of fresh water. It is organized in three parts. Part One covers a description of the area, the geology that made gravity irrigation possible, and what lured settlers who eventually would build the canal system. Part Two describes the formation of the company that would build the canal system, the construction and what bringing water to the land would mean. Part Three delves into the legal side of water, with the evolution of the doctrine within which the canal company operates. It covers some of the pressing issues that developed as the state grew and that still threaten many water users, including the canal company. And it takes a glimpse into the future.

Of all the irrigation projects in the country, the Twin Falls Canal Company stands out. This company holds a special place in western water history, which is rife with scandal, fraud and profligate government waste, turning public resources into vast private wealth. In contrast, this canal company, built by private investors, is the largest irrigation company in the country still owned by irrigators, and it is the largest and one of the most successful of the irrigation projects built in the West under the Carey Act of 1894. It remains among the largest gravity-fed irrigation systems in the world since Babylonian days. Its construction proved that it was possible for private individuals to build a significant canal system without the largesse of the federal government—beyond granting of land for settlers.

Courtesy Twin Falls Canal Co.

A steam shovel, similar to ones used on the Twin Falls tract, works in southern Idaho.

Part One: The Land

The I.B. Perrine Memorial Bridge spans the Snake River north of Twin Falls

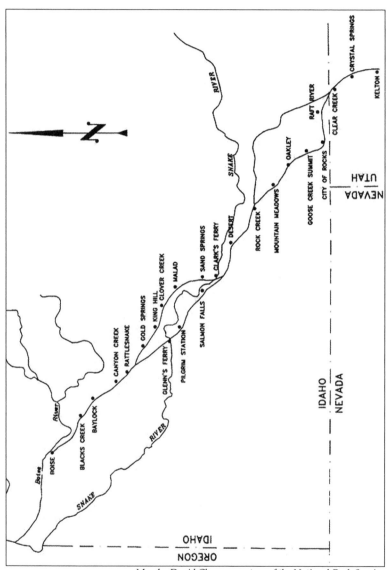

Map by David Chance courtesy of the National Park Service

Kelton Road through southern Idaho

Chapter One:
Perrine Coulee

"It was cooperation — and plenty of government largesse — that won and settled the West, not rugged individualists toting a Colt Peacemaker."

— Bernard DeVoto

Wild asparagus grows along some of the ditch banks that separate irrigated fields painted in hues of green and gray, brown and gold under piercing blue sky and broiling sun. Winds blow unobstructed out of the high desert to the west, stirring the dust and rattling tall old cottonwoods, alternately caressing and scouring the landscape. Sagebrush hills rise beyond the farms that cover a strip of land eight to twelve miles wide, stretching more than forty miles along the south side of the Snake River about halfway across southern Idaho. But the river, the defining feature here, below the line of sight. It runs at the bottom of a five-hundred-foot-deep canyon, a quarter mile wide, carved through eons of layered lava flows. From a high spot, land far to the north of the canyon is visible without a hint of the intervening chasm. This is the story of how that river came to irrigate the land along the canyon rims high above it.

The Snake River enters eastern Idaho as a controlled, and often fought over, release from Palisades Dam on the Wyoming border. It flows through the scenic Swan Valley and escapes into a wilderness of braided channels and the largest remnant riparian cottonwood forest in Idaho. Here cottonwoods still grow large and straight enough to carve a canoe like the ones that took early explorers down the river. Moose and coyote leave their tracks in the soft mud along the banks, and bald eagles circle overhead. But soon the river enters the lands of irrigated agriculture where it is sucked into the gaping maws of diversion canals and put to work. About midway across the state, a rock- and earth-fill dam about 80 feet high, spans the river. Milner Dam is more than a century old and raises the level of the river about 35 feet. It stops the second largest river in the West dead in its tracks. For nearly a century, nothing but leaks got past this venerable structure during the irrigation season.

The Snake River carries an average of 37 million acre-feet of water per year—two and half times as much as the Colorado River. At Milner, about 150 miles east of Boise, its entire flow is diverted and spread on farmed lands north and south of the river. Beyond the dam, the river drops into its narrow, vertical canyon. Here, reborn of gin-clear springs and runoff thick with mud, the river again offers a taste of serenity accessible only by boat. A riparian paradise hides mule deer, raccoon, muskrat, mink, beaver, otter, porcupine and the occasional cougar. Colonies of swallows build their mud nests under overhanging rock. The strident chatter of a belted kingfisher echoes across the water, and, with the patience of a Zen master, a great blue heron stalks the wetlands for a meal. High above, outlined against the sky, red-tail hawks ride thermal updrafts along the canyon walls. Though only a small percentage of the land, such riparian environments are crucial to the survival of most wildlife species in this high, arid country.

About 30 miles downstream, layered basalt atop a foundation of gnarled rhyolite lava formations gives way to golf courses and a municipal sewage treatment plant, while above, trophy homes line the canyon rim. The river rolls on, oblivious. Up on the rim the chaos of the wildland below disappears, replaced by engineered precision imposed on the natural landscape, with cultivated lands meticulously laid out in graph-paper grids of square-mile sections. Water that would have run in the river below now irrigates the fertile volcanic soil. Regimented rows of beans and potatoes, corn and beets, carpets of alfalfa and grains cover the landscape in quilted patchwork squares within the confines of the ditches that bring the water to this thirsty land.

A few miles south of the canyon rim, a small stream once ran free across this gently sloping basalt plain to the Snake River. It was so insignificant that most early explorers and inhabitants either missed it or ignored it, yet it drained some twenty-two thousand acres of sagebrush grassland. Most years it ran only during the spring and wet winters. This simple coulee may itself be of little significance—a grown man still can step across it in most places. But a hundred years ago, the stream, now known as Perrine Coulee, was put to work as part of the Twin Falls Canal Company, supplying water to a small part of the 202,000 acres of farmland supplied by the entire canal system.

Today the creek flows most of the year, augmented with irrigation water diverted from the canal system. It springs from a head gate on the Low Line Canal, one of the system's two primary canals, and runs about twenty miles to the Snake River, mostly following its natural course. On its way it flows through Twin Falls, the city created by the irrigation system.

In the winter, Perrine Coulee runs a lazy trickle of water transparent as a campaign promise. In the summer, it rolls up its sleeves, running high and fast to deliver irrigation water and carry away runoff the color of café au lait. It winds past cultivated fields, through backyards, under streets and passes all but unseen through the lives of residents of Twin Falls, a small city of about forty thousand and regional economic center set firmly on a foundation of agriculture.

The stream enters the city's southeast corner, carrying up to 125 cubic feet per second destined for water users along ten laterals that tap into the coulee. It passes Russian olives, willows and cottonwoods on vacant lots, graces the backyards of ordinary folks, and gurgles past ball fields and the playground of an elementary school—mostly it runs free, but here chain-link keeps curious and incautious neighborhood children from its unpredictable flows.

Gravity does the work, as the creek winds along remnant fields of former farms. They are now engulfed and consumed by urban growth spurred by the economic activity the irrigation system has brought. The gentle slope and the area's fertile soils are ready-made for a gravity irrigation system. The climate is ideal, with lots of warm sun and relatively mild winters. The natural slope lets water diverted from the Snake River flow south and west, parallel to the river. The slope then takes the water to the northwest, back across the land toward the river, following man-made ditches and natural streams like Perrine Coulee, and irrigating thousands of acres along the way.

The coulee dives under a busy street, trickles through a small neighborhood park and plays hide-and-seek behind modest frame houses. It passes a trucking outfit where it once flushed manure from cattle trucks. It separates a quiet residential neighborhood of aging upscale homes from a small shopping center, where it has become a convenient dumping place for shopping carts and old tires, disposable diapers and empty bottles and other detritus of city life. A great yawning culvert swallows the creek and takes it under a supermarket parking lot. It reemerges on the tranquil campus of the College of Southern Idaho, where yellow water iris line its course in the spring.

Perrine Coulee escapes the strictures of tract housing and trailer parks to run its final stretch along fields already staked out by residential and commercial developers. In a final quest for freedom the stream leaps from the edge of the sheer canyon wall. Three hundred feet below, after collecting itself again, it forms a wild border to a golf course before joining the murky, pea green Snake River.

The coulee is named for Ira Burton Perrine, the man whose vision helped to create the canal system. Few local residents are aware of the significance of the quiet and unpretentious stream that is the most visible presence of the Twin Falls Canal Company. Twin Falls was created in 1904 to be the commercial center of the 350-square-mile agricultural tract. The unassuming coulee represents the company and local farmers as it meanders through the larger community that grew up on the industries supplied by agriculture: the John Deere dealers, seed companies, hardware stores and all the other businesses that supply the local population, from fast-food joints to used car lots.

In southern Idaho, a fiery past laid out a fertile volcanic plain that the earliest explorers looked upon as a wasteland. In 1843, Captain John C. Fremont passed this way and wrote in a report of his travels, "The Exploring Expedition to the Rocky Mountains," a description of southern Idaho west of Fort Hall: "Beyond this place there does not occur, for a distance of nearly 300 miles to the westward, a fertile spot of ground sufficiently large to produce the necessary quantity of grain, or pasturage enough to allow even a temporary repose to the emigrants." He was wrong, of course, but that was before European settlers figured out what the land could produce when irrigated.

The first people to pass through the area after the early explorers and fur trappers were pioneers on the Oregon Trail, following a route blazed by explorer and fur trader Robert Stuart and described by Fremont. Few stayed. When gold brought the earliest settlers to the area, small farms and ranches sprang up to feed and supply the prospectors and miners. The growing population led to the wholesale eradication of the indigenous Shoshone and Paiute people of southern Idaho. One gold mining community put a bounty on their scalps, with adult males bringing more than women and children. Eventually, the survivors were herded onto reservations.

More European prospectors came when gold was discovered in the gravels along the Snake River. They drew commerce, which brought settlements that supplied the miners. The earliest efforts at irrigation were used to grow hay for livestock raised to feed the miners. Those early farmers and ranchers looked for ways to irrigate the flour-fine soil. They diverted small streams using brush and dirt dams. But the difficulty of bringing water to large tracts of dry but otherwise suitable land limited settlement in southern Idaho and many parts of the West.

In the Boise area the first irrigation projects started in 1843. Efforts to tame the Boise River in southwestern Idaho were immortalized in Wallace Stegner's book *Angle of Repose*. That effort eventually was completed with help from the federal government. Mormon farmers moving north from Utah began diverting the upper Snake River near the Wyoming border in the 1870s. Farmers downstream near Blackfoot started diverting the river in 1880. Settlers at an Oregon Trail rest stop on Rock Creek, south of the present city of Twin Falls, started diverting that creek in the 1870s. The federal government tried several ways to entice people to settle the lands of the newly opened West, but the lack of effective irrigation slowed those efforts. The Homestead Act and the Desert Land Act helped, but without large-scale irrigation settlement was slow. In 1894, however, the Carey Act got the states involved and all but gave away public land to any who could successfully irrigate it. The act provided for contractors to sell the irrigation system to farmers to earn back their investment in the construction. Thus the act provided an incentive for private investors to build diversion and distribution systems. But the Carey Act, too, was largely ineffectual, mostly because of overly optimistic estimates of available water and inadequate financing to complete the projects. Throughout most of the arid West, irrigation was up to the federal government. Finally it was funded by the Newland Act of 1902.

There were some exceptions. Smaller, privately financed projects brought irrigation to places where few thought it possible. It still is possible to find such places, where irrigators own and operate the diversion structures and distribution systems that provide them with water in much the same way as the acequias built in the Southwest by Spanish settlers in the late sixteenth century. With the help of investors, groups of irrigators built irrigation systems. These varied from a single simple ditch supplying water for a few hundred acres to a large canal system capable of irrigating more than 200,000 acres. The requirements of these systems forced people to cooperate and depend on each other.

One hundred years ago, around 1900, a few residents of south-central Idaho saw the potential for large-scale irrigation if only a dam could be built to tame the Snake River. But dreams of damming the mighty Snake were beyond the cooperative efforts of the few neighboring farmers. Surveyors had laid out the possibilities. But no one knew how to attract the kind of capital needed to build a dam big enough to stop the Snake River.

Visionary Burt Perrine was determined to build such a dam. Skeptics said it would never hold; and if it did, the canals would wash out; and if the canal banks held, the ground would quickly turn alkali. Perrine's enthusiasm, however, eventually convinced eastern industrialist Frank Buhl and his partner, Peter Kimberly, to invest in a massive project at a place on the river called The Cedars. They had the money to hire the engineers, managers and workers. The dam was built and canals dug by men with shovels, horses, steam shovels, electric cranes and eastern financial backing. Perrine's vision set the effort in motion.

Today, like the acequias of the Southwest, the Twin Falls Canal Company is run by a board elected by the landowners, who irrigate the fields surrounding the city. The leaders, however, no longer elect a mayor domo each year. That role is filled by a professional manager hired by the board and paid by the shareholders' fees. Here, as in the Southwest, a communal structure has grown up around the irrigation system. The farmers who are shareholders in the canal company depend on their fellow shareholders for the system to function. And the communities that grew up on the Twin Falls tract depend on agriculture. The canal system is the source of the community's common prosperity. And its successful operation requires cooperation among its members. Anything that threatens the integrity of the system, either the water itself or the right to use it, threatens the entire system and the communities that depend on the water for their livelihood.

Karl Wittfogel in his 1957 book, *Oriental Despotism: A Comparative Study of Total Power*, put forth the notion that when nature forces a society to organize to control water, that society also has the means to establish a despotic rule. That hasn't happened, exactly, in southern Idaho. The common bond has knit a tight community that depends on the control of water, but the system of governing is anything but despotic. The canal company is a model of a democratic government where the shareholders, or parciantes, run things. The members share the costs of operations and repairs.

And so far, with a few repairs over the years, Milner Dam and the canals still are holding water; the soil still is productive. But pouring water where it had never flowed before brought a whole new set of problems. The water didn't always run where it was expected and showed up at times in unexpected places. The water also nourished new ecosystems, with plants and animals that often interfered with or threatened the orderly distribution of water. Other problems, especially erosion, appeared uninvited soon after water hit bare dirt. But crops thrived in the fertile soil and plentiful sun. Soon the former sagebrush-gray and bunch-grass-tawny plain began to sprout deep-green irrigated squares. Keeping it that way has required steady, ongoing effort.

Even with the physical issues in check, though never completely overcome, other more complex issues arose to threaten the canal company's right to divert the water it has come to depend on. The moment people began taking water from streams, neighbors began to fight over the supply during dry times. To resolve such issues, water users in the West adopted a doctrine first applied in the California gold fields. The doctrine of "prior appropriation," or first in time is first in right, eventually was applied throughout the arid West and is the basis of water law in Idaho. The doctrine is grounded in the premise of seniority—the water user who first put water to a recognized beneficial use is the first to get water during times of shortages. So-called "junior" water rights are then filled in descending order, from oldest to newest. In good years everyone gets their water. In dry years, only the most senior rights are filled and others go dry.

Ideally, the system forms a bridge between registered water rights, known as "paper water," and the highly variable flow of a natural river. It is a way of reconciling an inconsistent resource with legal water rights that are considered property rights. Yet, poor record keeping and the geological complexities of interconnected ground and surface water have led to one of the greatest water rights battles in the West. The struggle between groundwater users and surface water users erupted in the early 1980s in a huge, but by no means decisive, battle. And it is not over yet. Managing ground and surface water together became far more complex than anyone expected.

Competition for the limited amount of water continues to grow in Idaho and across the West, and indeed across the globe. It is nothing new. Water users long have fought with neighbors during times of shortages. But now, other claims—some of them legitimate, others not—are vying for the water. They include drinking water for Los Angeles, water for the frivolous fountains of Las Vegas, and water to help endangered salmon migrate to the ocean.

No one who depends on it takes water in the arid West for granted. In Idaho, when the pervasive application of irrigation water is included, the average use is about fifteen thousand gallons per day, per person. That's more than ten times the national average of about fourteen hundred gallons per day, per person. The amount of water used by southern Idaho irrigators varies depending on the soil and the crops raised. One cubic foot per second—about 450 gallons per minute—is enough to irrigate 60 to 100 acres on average. In water-short years, however, farmers pay more attention to their water and often get better yields with less water. By comparison, in some dry countries careful irrigators can stretch a cubic foot per second over 200 to 300 acres with better distribution systems, such as drip irrigation, and careful management.

Water and the power to move it provide the underpinnings of the southern Idaho economy. About thirty thousand farms irrigate about four million acres in southern Idaho's Snake River Valley. Together they raise crops worth more than $350 million, including potatoes, hay, wheat, barley, sugar beets, beans, feed corn, alfalfa and a few others. About 2000, agriculture provided 29 percent of the income and 27.5 percent of the jobs; turning those agricultural products into food products provided 26.7 percent of income and 24.5 percent of jobs. The Snake and Columbia rivers bind southern Idaho to the rest of the Pacific Northwest economically and ecologically. Irrigated farms in the Pacific Northwest earn about $5 billion annually. Food processing earns $4.6 billion and employs more than sixty thousand people, producing half the nation's frozen vegetables.

Much of it is made possible by the ample precipitation in the mountains of the region, more than sixty inches per year in some places. Most of it falls as snow, and the melt-water is captured in reservoirs and meted out into vast networks of ever-smaller irrigation canals. An average 3.3 million acre-feet of water is diverted from the Snake River in southern and eastern Idaho, and an average 600,000 acre-feet is pumped from the Eastern Snake River Plain Aquifer during the irrigation season. Another 4 million acre-feet is held in federal storage reservoirs on the upper Snake.

The cost of irrigating the land varies with location. The Twin Falls Canal Company supplies water to 202,690 acres for about $24 per acre—a total of about $4.86 million. That $24 buys about four acre-feet per irrigation season. In comparison, on nearby bluffs about six hundred feet above the Snake River, farmers on the Bell Rapids Project in western Twin Falls County pay $1.5 million to $2.3 million for electricity to lift water from the river and spread it on about 18,000 acres. Those farmers in 1998 paid $152 per share, which bought about two and a half acre-feet of water. But rising power costs have outpaced farm profits, and in 2005, they sold their water rights to the state to help provide more flows for migrating endangered salmon.

Irrigation water comes at other costs as well. Over the past one hundred years, wasteful irrigation practices of intensive, industrialized agriculture have stripped topsoil from the land and choked the river with sediment and nutrient-laden runoff. Yet, in a contrast that is not unlike the tenuous balance between life and death in the high desert, this irrigation system has brought to life communities and an economy that continue to prosper. And keeping the dam and the canals operating is a teeter-totter of ongoing maintenance and crisis management. It requires a balance of diplomacy and hard-edged legal and political maneuvering with the competing users of a limited resource. It requires maintaining the uneasy truce between the mindless power of natural systems, the limits of human ingenuity and the physical limits of a system built of dirt, rocks, concrete and steel. In some places water falls as rain, but in many places, such as southern Idaho, it has to be pumped from the ground or diverted from streams and transported to fields. In many places water is taken for granted. In Twin Falls, the local canal system, though it has national and historic significance, winds largely unnoticed through the community. But the importance becomes visible in the response of residents when the system is threatened by a canal break or a leak in the dam that supplies the water.

Bisbee photo courtesy Twin Falls Public Library.

Storm clouds gather over Milner Dam in southern Idaho.

Chapter Two:
Saving the Dam

A powerful stream of water as thick as his thigh spewed from a pipe where he should have seen only a trickle. That stream could mean only one thing: The dam had sprung a leak. But where? Dam tender Joe Yost knew right away he had a serious problem on his hands. It was just after 7 a.m. on September 24, 1998. The "toe drain" on the downstream side of Milner Dam is a six-inch-diameter pipe that drains seepage from the interior of the rock-and earth-fill dam. This was more than seepage, and Yost knew it was more than he could handle alone. William E. Brock describes the situation in his story, "Workers plug dam leak. Hole at Milner never threatened canal system," in the Twin Falls *Times-News*, on September 28. The dam held back about 34,000 acre-feet of potential trouble in a reservoir known as the Milner pool. Yost called the two canal companies that own and operate the then-93-year-old dam to sound the alarm.

Though local people were concerned about the threats to downstream residents, bridges and other structures, their response to Yost's alarm was a measure of the importance of the dam to the community, and in a larger sense it illustrated the role and the importance of water in the arid West. Without question, everyone knew a serious dam break was the largest threat to the area's agricultural economy. One week of relentless Idaho wind can suck the moisture from a whole winter's worth of snow out of the soil. The only thing that makes agriculture possible here is the Snake River and the dam and canal systems that bring life-giving water from the mountains of western Wyoming. Without that water there would be little here other than the sagebrush grasslands that greeted white settlers. There would be only a few scattered ranches in stream- and spring-fed valleys, and small farms where water could be diverted directly out onto fields.

Without waiting for help to arrive, Yost started opening spillway gates a little after 8 a.m. to lower the level of the reservoir behind the dam. Just over 400 cubic feet per second of water flowed past the dam into the Snake River Canyon below. A half hour later that grew to 6,800 cubic feet. And by 9:30 a.m., more than 16,000 cubic feet—or 7 million gallons per minute—was gushing through the dam gates.

Yost's job was to keep an eye on things at the dam. He had merely to step out his back door and take a few steps. He lived in a yellow frame house set under some black locust trees a scant twenty yards from the dam. As dam tender he monitored the reservoir level to make sure it was high enough to flow into the canals, but not too high. He controlled the reservoir level by opening or closing spillway gates, which stayed closed most of the time--except as this morning, in emergencies. His job was crucial, but made easier by the Bureau of Reclamation, which operates the Minidoka Dam a few miles upstream. The Bureau typically releases only what irrigators need at the Milner pool. The river is held back in reservoirs farther upstream on the Snake River.

Less than thirty minutes after the call from Yost, Twin Falls Canal Company maintenance supervisor Clay Robinson and field supervisor Stan Haye arrived at the dam. By the time the two men arrived, a section of dirt had slid away from the face of the dam, exposing a four-foot-tall concrete retaining wall. A vortex swirled out in the reservoir, and water had begun undermining the wall. A hole was starting to blossom on the downstream side. The trouble spot was in the south section of the three-section dam, about forty feet from the old spillway gates. The two men didn't wait for the bulldozers and other heavy equipment that still were miles away. They had brought a load of bentonite clay—a cat litter-like substance—and began dumping it into the growing hole in the dam. Despite their efforts, the hole grew to more than twenty feet across before heavy equipment arrived.

After Robinson and Haye, the next person notified, though out of town that day, was a short man with black hair and a keen sense of purpose. Vince Alberdi is responsible for ensuring the steady and dependable supply of water to more than two hundred thousand acres of farmland. A smile almost always plays around his eyes, but the canal company manager also carries the weight of responsibility. He knows as well as anyone the importance of the dam and the availability of water to the communities of the Twin Falls area.

Word of a potential dam break rippled up and down the Snake River. About thirty-five miles upstream, the U.S. Bureau of Reclamation was releasing about six thousand cubic feet per second from the federal Minidoka Dam. Most of that was being diverted into the irrigation canals at Milner Dam — about 5,400 cubic feet had been going into the North Side Canal Company and Twin Falls canal systems before Yost opened the gates. The Bureau cut back the flows at Minidoka. Downstream, Idaho Power Company began to make room for more water by lowering the level of the reservoirs at its hydroelectric facilities at Twin Falls, Shoshone Falls, Upper Salmon Falls, Lower Salmon Falls and Bliss dams. The Twin Falls County sheriff's office began warning residents in low-lying areas along the river of potential flooding.

Constricted by the narrow and rugged Snake River Canyon, high flows threatened homes along the river, golf courses and the main water supply pipe for the city of Twin Falls which crosses the river about thirty miles downstream from Milner Dam. The river level under the pipe rose fourteen inches that morning. Twin Falls police halted traffic down to public parks at Shoshone Falls and Twin Falls and other areas near the river. The Canyon Springs Golf Course on the edge of the river sent its grounds crews home, and warned golfers of the potential danger. Most of the golfers went home as well.

Milner Dam spans the Snake, about where the river hits the half-way point on its way across southern Idaho, at a place once called The Cedars for the trees on two islands in the river. They were actually junipers that resemble eastern cedars, which aren't real cedars either. The dam construction eventually washed away the trees. This is the spot where the river plunges into a narrow, steep-walled, 500-foot-deep canyon. It's the last place a dam could be used to stop and divert enough water to irrigate the large expanse of lava plain above the river.

The dam's three sections connect the two islands and the north and south banks. It raises the level of the river thirty-eight feet by closing the three channels of the river with rock-fill dams. The two islands hold spillways and control structures. Altogether the dam runs about two thousand feet long, one hundred fifty feet wide, and eighty-three feet high. It stops the river, which left unfettered would be flowing at near ten thousand cubic feet per second or more on average. Passing essentially just leakage, the dam left the sun-baked riverbed dry until it was rebuilt in the 1990s. The river is reborn downstream from clear springs, murky sediment- and nutrient-laden runoff from fields, excess irrigation water and a few natural streams.

Milner Dam holds back about 38,000 acre-feet of water when full.

Though humble in appearance, the simple dam harnessed — but never tamed — the raging Snake River. The water it backs up supplies five irrigation companies. The largest is the Twin Falls Canal Company, next is the North Side Canal Company. Together, those two irrigate more than 330,000 acres. Next are the A&B Irrigation District, Milner Irrigation District and American Falls Reservoir District No. 2. All five combined divert about ten thousand cubic feet per second from the pool behind Milner during the height of the irrigation season—that's 4.5 million gallons per minute. And they irrigate more than 400,000 acres of farmland in a region that gets ten to twelve inches of precipitation in a good year. Most of those acres would go dry until the dam was fixed– the situation was not as critical in September as it would have been in July or August, when even a week without water would damage or destroy most crops. But even in September many farmers still need their full supply of water to let their crops ripen.

The Snake River carries water through southern Idaho from the ample precipitation in the Snake, Teton and Caribou mountains to the east—some places get more than sixty inches per year. The mountain ranges—ninety miles long, thirteen thousand feet high—wring water from Pacific storms. Most of it falls as snow in winter, and the meltwater is captured in reservoirs and meted out into vast networks of irrigation canals. The system of federal reservoirs on the upper Snake River can hold 4.2 million acre-feet of water. Farmers hold the rights to all the flows and the bulk of the water stored in those reservoirs, operated by the federal Bureau of Reclamation.

At Milner Dam, the Twin Falls Canal Company diverts up to 3,600 cubic feet per second—about 1.6 million gallons per minute—and delivers it to more than 202,000 acres through about 107 miles of main canals. The system comprises nine miles of the Main Line Canal from Milner Dam to the seven-thousand-acre-foot Murtaugh Lake; fifteen miles of Main Line from the lake to The Forks where the canal splits; thirty-six miles of the Low Line Canal; and forty-seven miles of the High Line Canal. About eleven hundred miles of smaller secondary canals, known as laterals, bring water to the head gates that supply the farmers. The company holds a water right for three thousand cubic feet of natural river flow that a young Burt Perrine filed in 1900, making it one of the oldest on that part of the river. It also has a contract for storage of about 250,000 acre-feet of water in American Falls Reservoir and Jackson Lake, Wyoming. That's about a month's supply during peak season. (The irrigation season typically runs from mid-March to October.)

The canal system metes out the water in measures of flow

known as a miner's inch, and fractions thereof. One cubic foot per second equals fifty miner's inches, typically enough to irrigate eighty acres — or five-eighths of an inch is enough for one acre. The canal company normally delivers three-quarters of an inch per acre. Most years, the company has been able to deliver the full amount. Low water in 1977, one of the driest years on record, forced the company to cut back to half an inch. That's forty inches for eighty acres. With careful management, that's plenty for most irrigators. In August 1988, low water again forced the canal company to cut deliveries to a half inch. In 1992, the company cut back to two-thirds inch and later to half an inch. In that year, many farmers, forced to manage their water more carefully, reported better than average yields from their potato fields.

Vince Alberdi's job is to make sure the canal system runs smoothly. He grew up in a sheep-herding family on the north side of the river in Jerome County. He learned about the importance and the power of water when his father sold the livestock business and went to work for the canal company. The young Alberdi worked summers chaining or "mossing" — that is clearing algae and aquatic weeds from the canals and laterals of the North Side Canal Company by dragging heavy chains with a pair of tractors, one on each side of the ditch. After high school he earned degrees in business administration and civil engineering — a useful combination for the manager of a canal company with an annual budget of $5 million and eighty employees. He takes his responsibility seriously. He is a good manager, he understands people and he surrounds himself with competent assistants and steps aside to let them do their jobs. On the scene of a canal break or dam leak, he sometimes feels like he is in the way, but his sense of responsibility will not let him stay away.

Alberdi learned the complexities of running a canal system working as the number two man at the North Side Canal Company under manager Ted Diehl, now his counterpart. Alberdi's stint as Diehl's assistant from 1987 to fall of 1992 provided a good foundation for the job as head of the largest private canal company in the country. The two now share responsibility for the operation of Milner Dam. The job is "like riding a bucking horse and trying to make it go in a straight line," Alberdi said. But he wouldn't trade it for anyone else's.

He knows what makes irrigators tick and the tricks water plays on even the most honest individuals. Ditch riders sometimes have to chain and lock the head gates to keep some farmers from giving the crank a few extra turns to get a little more water. But the same guys might find the ditch rider's wallet and return it with all the money still in it.

When he's not out meeting with farmers or government officials or canal company employees, Alberdi works at his desk in the new canal company office a few blocks from its original 1909 building on a downtown Twin Falls corner. As running the company in modern times became more complex, the operation outgrew the historic building. Other improvements Alberdi has overseen include modernizing the company's maintenance shops and replacing original head gates with precast concrete gates instead of pouring them in place.

The structures that regulate the flow of water through the system are slowly being replaced with automated controls. Parts of the canal system, dug by men and mules a hundred years ago, now are run by remote control from a central computer. Eventually the entire system will be run by computer. System managers will be able to make changes without leaving the office, improving efficiency and allowing operators to respond more quickly to requests for water from farmers anywhere on the system. The automated controls also are rigged to warn operators about problems. So, the next time Milner Dam springs a leak, a system manager will be able to respond from the central office, opening spill gates before people have time to arrive on the ground. But no computer can do what the construction crews faced that morning in September 1998.

Milner Dam steadfastly supplied irrigation water to several hundred thousand acres without much visible change for the better part of a century. Over the years leaks and problems were repaired, broken equipment was replaced, motors replaced hand cranks and weakened concrete was repoured. In 1992, the North Side and Twin Falls canal companies—with the help of Idaho Power Company, southern Idaho's dominant investor-owned utility—completed a major overhaul of the then eighty-seven-year-old dam. The years had taken their toll, and minor repairs were no longer enough.

Over the years, various leaks developed. Most were minor and soon repaired. The first happened in 1905 as the dam was completed. The bypass gates were reopened and repairs started immediately to seal the dam with cinders and silt. On March 15, 1983, water penetrated the wooden core and flowed through the dam at about two hundred cubic feet per second. The leak was discovered as the reservoir filled in preparation for the irrigation season. Apparently a muskrat hole had broken the seal formed by silt allowing water to penetrate the interior of the dam. Piping action eroded dirt from the rock and created a small cavern within the dam. The hole was refilled with gravel and rock, and then the dam was shaped to its original contour. It could have been serious, but the damage was quickly repaired and the incident did not delay the start of the irrigation season. It did prompt canal company officials to take a closer look at the then nearly eighty-year-old dam, however. They hired a Boise engineering firm, CH2M Hill, to study it.

In their 1983 study, the engineers found that some of the wooden planks in the dam's original core were rotten. When Milner was built, a core of two-by-six boards stacked lengthwise, edge to edge, formed the interior of the dam. Where the boards made contact with dirt, they had rotted. In places where they had contacted only rock, they were as good as new. But the wooden core was mostly rotted away, and the only seal was the silt that had settled into the upstream face of the dam. If water penetrated the silt, the dam could spring a major leak. The engineers also noted that the dam was vulnerable to earthquakes. They feared shaking during an earthquake would liquefy the mud that sealed the dam face and allow water to seep through the entire dam. In addition, the canals needed $61 million in repairs.

An unrelated project gave canal company officials an idea for how to pay for the repairs. Since 1977 canal company officials had talked about adding a power plant on the system to take advantage of the natural fall of water. In 1983, officials from the canal company and Idaho Power Company agreed to build a power plant where the main canal splits, and one side drops 80 feet into the Low Line Canal. Idaho Power agreed to buy the power. The eight megawatt plant was completed in 1984, and the arrangement has earned revenue for both companies. The canal company leaders learned about the advantages of generating power and began to look for other opportunities.

Then in 1988, a Federal Energy Regulatory Commission — FERC — dam safety inspection echoed the results of the study done five years earlier. The commission found Milner Dam at an unacceptable risk of failing during an earthquake. FERC regulates private dams and hydroelectric projects on the nation's rivers. The likelihood of a catastrophic break was remote. But, depending on the time of year, a serious leak could cause a sizable blowout, raising river levels downstream and putting the irrigation system out of action for several weeks while repairs were made.

The estimated cost to repair the dam and meet FERC's requirements came to about $11 million. That was steep, even split among the 7,500 shareholders of the two canal companies. To pay for the repairs, the Twin Falls and North Side canal companies worked out a deal with Idaho Power. The power company would pay for the repairs and build a separate hydroelectric plant. The canal company in turn would supply Idaho Power with water not needed for irrigation, water that otherwise would be spilled over Milner Dam.

It was an ambitious project. The two-unit power plant sits below the south canyon rim about a mile and a half downstream from Milner Dam. The power plant can generate up to 57.5 megawatts. To take advantage of varying flows, it has two different sized turbines. One turbine can generate 46 megawatts, and the other 11.5 megawatts. A megawatt is 1 million watts — enough power to light up ten thousand, 100 watt light bulbs. During low flows, only the smaller unit runs. As flows increase, the plant switches to the larger turbine. And at the highest flows, both turbines run. The large new power plant can handle a maximum flow of 5,200 cubic feet per second. The mile and a half of widened main canal to the plant accommodates up to 9,000 cubic feet per second, bypassing about a mile and a half of the Snake River — a narrow stretch known as the Milner Gorge. New canal control gates are just beyond the power plant intakes.

When it approved the changes at the dam and the new power plant, FERC added the requirement that 200 cubic feet per second be allowed to pass Milner Dam in the otherwise dry stretch between the dam and the power plant outlet. But the flow is required only when the water is available. A smaller turbine in the new spillway of the rebuilt Milner Dam takes advantage of the minimum flow required by the dam's new federal permit. The 800 kilowatt unit runs anytime the flow is available.

Workers prepare Milner Dam for new concrete during reconstruction.

A massive concrete and steel spillway and new spillway gates were added on the north island. The old spillway gates remain in place as emergency spill gates. The dam's new gates can spill 116,750 cubic feet per second. Using the original structure as a base, the dam's sloping sides were built up, tapering toward the crest. Most of the work was done on the downstream side, where additional rock thickened the embankment. Keeping the water at bay under the new rock is a layer of silt held in place by successively coarser rock covered with more rock and rubble. To drain the water that inevitably soaks into the center of the dam, engineers included a "toe drain" to prevent that water from building up. The six-inch pipe drains at river level on the downstream side of the dam.

Reconstruction also made Joe Yost's job considerably easier. The original spillway was on top of the south island. Its ninety-nine wooden gates were closed and opened manually, one at a time—a laborious process using a hydraulic hoist on a track. The operator positioned the lumbering behemoth over each gate by turning its axle with a three-foot pipe wrench. Once in position and hooked onto the gate, a small electric motor drove the hydraulic cylinder that raised and lowered the gate. Today the spillway gates are operated electrically.

The dam reconstruction and power plant project, completed in 1992, cost about $56 million—more than ten times the cost of the original dam and canal system. The new concrete and rock fill gives the venerable Milner Dam a fresh modern look and still stops the river dead in its tracks.

When the bulldozers, excavators and dump trucks full of rock and dirt finally began arriving on September 24, 1998, Clay Robinson and Stan Haye were losing ground. A tracked excavator from the North Side Canal Company began dumping more bentonite followed by rocks and dirt into the muddy soup at the bottom of the hole in the dam, to little apparent effect; the dirt just quivered like jelly. But finally the battle began to turn. More rock, gravel and dirt went into the hole as the crews began to gain the upper hand. After a few hours, they choked off the muddy discharge from the toe drain to little more than a trickle.

Had the dam broken, the constricting canyon would have taken some of the energy out of the surge of water. The three dam segments almost certainly would not have given way all at once; in fact, one could have slowly crumbled without affecting the other two sections of the eighty-six-foot-tall dam. The flow might not have been greater than it had been in some years in the recent past, since the thirty-four thousand acre-feet sitting behind the dam would have drained over many hours. In the spring of 1997, for example, thirty-five thousand cubic feet per second gushed through Milner Dam. At that rate, the reservoir would have drained in twelve hours. Downstream, people would have seen a rise of a few feet in the river level. The sudden rise would have been enough to do some localized flooding but not enough to do widespread damage.

The high water in 1997 threatened the city of Twin Falls' water pipeline, which spans the river on an old bridge a few feet above the normal river level. Not just the flow, but floating debris snagging on the pipeline or on the bridge piers holding it up created pressure, threatening the stability of the structure. Volunteers in boats stopped large floating debris. The pipeline supplied more than 70 percent of the city's water at the time. The bridge could survive 32,000 cubic feet per second, but probably not 40,000 or 50,000, and certainly not 100,000 cubic feet, City Engineer Gary Young said at the time. High water also would threaten the city's sewage treatment plant on the river's south bank.

On the morning of September 24, the town held its breath as the drama played out—until word came back that the dam was in no danger of breaking. The relief was palpable.

On this September morning the crews of the Twin Falls and North Side canal companies and a few volunteers had averted trouble. By 10:30 a.m., Yost was closing the spillway gates again and the flow past the dam had started back down. The flow had been as high as 16,114 cubic feet, but by 11:30 a.m. it was down to just under nine hundred cubic feet per second. A little past noon the Bureau of Reclamation had returned the releases at Minidoka to just about six thousand feet. Bad as it had looked, the dam never was threatened. "I've fixed five holes on this dam in the thirty years I've been here," Ted Diehl, manager of the North Side Canal Company told the Twin Falls *Times-News* at the time. "This one wasn't too bad, but they get bigger if you let 'em go."

Harnessed, but not entirely tamed, the river again flowed into the canals on both sides of the river. Water again entered the arid land through a network of large canals, smaller canals and ditches, like blood vessels. Row crops, grains and alfalfa hay have replaced the hardy sagebrush and native bunch grasses. The settlers replaced the aboriginal inhabitants. The early irrigators gave little thought to how much water was left in the river or the effects of agricultural runoff.

But the story of Milner Dam and the Twin Falls Canal Company starts nearly 200 years earlier, when the first white Europeans ventured into southern Idaho, looking for an easier way across the country.

Horses and scrapers on the Twin Falls Tract. *Courtesy Twin Falls Canal Co.*

Chapter Three:
Beginnings

Antoine Clappine heard the shouted warning. But it came too late. It would cost him his life. Ramsey Crooks, seated near the front of the canoe, watched helplessly as the current drove them straight at a rock pillar rising from the roiling waters. The best efforts of Clappine, a skilled French-Canadian voyageur, could not avert disaster. The cottonwood log canoe split lengthwise, spilling the five people and their gear into the raging river. Crooks and one of the others swam to safety. Two clambered onto the rock and were later rescued. Seeing the disaster, the rest of the party pulled their canoes from the water. The current carried off most of the gear from the wrecked canoe and swept Clappine away. He drowned on October 28, 1811, the first white European to die in the unexplored territory that would become southern Idaho.

The trouble struck in the Snake River a little more than a mile below the site known later as The Cedars. Here the river drops into a narrow, steep-walled rock chasm known now as the Milner Gorge, where the entire flow of the Snake River is squeezed between vertical rock walls maybe fifty yards wide.

Clappine and his fellow travelers, in canoes hewn from large cottonwood logs much like the ones used by the Lewis and Clark expedition a few years earlier, had hoped to float all the way down the Snake to the Columbia River and then to Fort Astoria at the mouth of the Columbia. Lead by Wilson Price Hunt, a partner in John Jacob Astor's newly minted Pacific Fur Company, the explorers were on their way to the mouth of the Columbia to help establish a fur trading post and settlement to be named Astoria. They also hoped to scout a more practical overland route than

Lewis and Clark had followed. Hunt's party got out of the river about a mile below the accident. They abandoned the canoes, cached the remaining supplies they couldn't carry and set out on foot for the mouth of the Columbia.

Hunt and his party had left St. Louis in October 1810 and were to meet another party that had left the East Coast by ship a month earlier and headed around Cape Horn, with a planned stop in the Sandwich Islands. The second party had arrived by sea at the mouth of the Columbia River in March 1811 and set up shop at Astoria long before the fatal canoe accident. Members of Hunt's party began arriving the following January. The last stragglers showed up in May. The party already in Astoria included a young Scot named Robert Stuart, who was a partner with Astor. He was to return overland to New York to report to Astor.

Stuart set out from Astoria on June 29, 1812, with six men, all veterans of Hunt's westbound trip. By the end of August they were back in southern Idaho. On August 28, they made camp at the crossing of a creek they called Precipice Creek—now known as Rock Creek—about five miles southeast of the present site of Twin Falls. In his notes Stuart writes of the sagebrush plain: though commonly called a prairie, "but forest of wormwood is more properly its name." He applied the European term, wormwood, for sagebrush, *Artemisia tridentata*, which still dominates the uncultivated lands of the arid West. Stuart looked across a landscape shaped by geology, time, wind and water. The plain rose gently toward low hills less than ten miles to the south, and the whole plain sloped imperceptibly to the west. Behind him distant mountains rose on the northern horizon. They might still have had a little snow on their peaks. Between him and those mountains, the desert hid two of its most dramatic features: the Snake River Canyon, a quarter mile across and 500 feet deep, and the river that took Clappine's life.

From where he stood, the summer flow in Rock Creek would have been only a few yards wide. But he would have been able to see the cleft in the hills where that creek runs out onto the plain. Those hills rise to nearly eight thousand feet above sea level, more than four thousand feet above the surrounding plain. The rise starts so gently their height is deceiving. The major drainage in the hills flows northwest toward the Snake River. In its upper reaches,

Rock Creek winds through lush meadows and languishes behind beaver dams before crashing down across rocky rapids and under the cool shade of stream-side willows. Tributaries tumble playfully out of side canyons. Spectacular rock formations, outcroppings and hoodoos stud the narrow valley of Rock Creek. Willow thickets and cottonwoods line the creek. Western junipers climb the slopes to stands of lodgepole pine and subalpine fir in the higher elevations. Up here, serviceberry and mountain mahogany contribute important deer winter forage. In wetter areas, large stands of aspen tremble in the breezes. Some of the shadier north-facing bottoms hide remnant stands of Douglas fir. Wetlands along the creeks and wet meadows surround springs and streams and beaver ponds. Between the sagebrush and the aspen communities, the ranks are filled with rabbitbrush, four-wing saltbush, mountain snowberry, wild rose, squawbush and others that contribute to the texture and richness of these hills.

Stuart and his party would have found herds of mule deer and elk, bighorn sheep, black bears and the occasional grizzly, along with wolves and mountain lions. Coyotes, rarely tolerated by wolves, were relegated to the fringes. The numerous small mammals and birds would have included rock chucks, jack rabbits, sage grouse, turkey vultures, red-tail hawks, Swainson's hawk in the summer, rough-legged hawks in the winter, Coopers and sharp-shinned hawks and northern goshawk. The sagebrush would have resounded with the song of the Western meadow lark, the vesper sparrow and other migrating songbirds.

The creek at Stuart's feet emerged gin-clear where the hills meet the wide volcanic plain. For several miles the creek flows near the surface of the plain. By the time it reaches the Snake River it has dropped into a canyon with near-vertical walls as deep as the Snake River Canyon's. Here the creek is all but inaccessible from above. But just before the creek enters the deepening canyon, it flows through an oasis, where for years Indians found shade from cottonwoods, willows for sweat lodges and in later years, grass for their horses. Here was a good place to rest and an easy place to cross the creek.

Stuart would have looked out over land dominated by Wyoming big sagebrush and a variety of native perennial grasses, shrubs and wild flowers—a gray-green carpet, touched by the tawny color of seasoned grasses. The dusty-green sagebrush stand three or four feet tall, with some as tall as a man. The sweet pungent aroma of sage scents the desert air, especially after a summer thunderstorm. Under the stringy gray-brown bark is tough wood that makes good firewood: It's easy to light, and it burns hot. Sagebrush covers perhaps 10 to 15 percent of the land. In between are grasses that include bluebunch wheat grass, Idaho fescue, Thurber needlegrass and Great Basin wild rye. And among the grasses a variety of shrubs and wild flowers poke up; some flower only in the wettest years. In the driest spots, prickly pear might form a carpet.

Down on the ground, a gray mat of cryptogamic crust covers the soil, a fragile tangle of algae and moss that soaks up and holds moisture and keeps a grip on the soil. It stops all but the worst erosion by wind and water. On a trip through southern Idaho around the beginning of the twentieth century, naturalist John Burroughs noted the lack of sod. Bunch grasses grew in tufts with the ground showing around them. But it wasn't all bare dirt. Where it remained undisturbed, the ground was covered with this thin, fragile crust. Beneath the crust, fine loamy volcanic soil averaged ten feet deep. In some places, the underlying rock poked up through the soil—the very sinew and bone of this lean, arid country. Had Stuart crossed the river, he would have found lighter, sandier and thinner soil on the north side.

Eons of weathering of the volcanic hills to the south formed great alluvial fans in a gentle slope to meet the Snake River to the north. But the plain is by no means unbroken. It is punctuated with what local residents call buttes; geologists call them extinct shield volcanoes. They are giant magma pustules that once oozed out the lava that forms the flat and gently sloping lands around them—layer upon layer, eon after eon. They tell a story of the region's volcanic past, a story that began seventeen million years ago.

Scientists argue about the cause, but a weak spot in the earth's crust started in what is now southeastern Oregon and resulted in a festering hot spot beneath the continental crust. The hot spot erupted periodically, at times violently, sending hot ash and lava out across the landscape. The process continued as the southwesterly continental drift moved over the hot spot. The crust moved over hot spot, like a sheet of metal passing over a hot torch. Violent eruptions blew rhyolite ash, which solidified into rock known as tuff, across much of southwestern Idaho and into parts of Nevada and southeastern Oregon. A string of ancient extinct volcanoes, becoming progressively younger, form a nearly straight line east from southeastern Oregon, ending beneath the plateau that is Yellowstone National Park. Today the hot spot is the source of the park's geothermal features, such as the Old Faithful geyser.

In later years, basalt lava oozed from rifts opened by less violent eruptions associated with basin and range faulting, as the continent spread to the southwest. American Indians of the region still tell legends of the mountains of fire. The heavy viscous lava spread in huge sheets, covering the older, gray rhyolite with thin layers of darker basalt. Repeated lava flows built up the Eastern Snake River Plain. At more than ten thousand square miles, it is larger than the state of Maryland. In the intervening years, sediments from Ice Age floods, gravels of ancient stream beds and windblown soil collected on the surface; only to be covered by the next lava flow. The most recent flows are about two thousand years old. The evidence can be seen today at Craters of the Moon National Monument near the town of Arco. The combined result of the recurring basalt flows is dramatically displayed in the layer cake of rock exposed in the Snake River Canyon. Here the flat, horizontal basalt flows of varying thickness lie stacked over the irregular rhyolite formations.

Eventually, rain and snow melt seeped into the ground and filled the cracks in the basalts and the sediments between the layers to form what today is the Eastern Snake River Plain Aquifer. This aquifer gives rise to numerous springs along the Snake River, most notably Thousand Springs west of Twin Falls. The aquifer lies beneath a lava plain sixty miles wide and sweeps across two hundred miles, about half the width of the state, from northwest of Idaho Falls to the King Hill area east of Glenns Ferry. Hydrologists estimate the top one hundred feet of the aquifer contains about one hundred million acre-feet of water. In the 1990s, about 2,600 cubic feet per second flowed from springs near American Falls into the river, and about 5,200 cubic feet gushed from the Thousand Springs area near Hagerman. But decades of irrigation, beginning in the 1870s, had poured thousands of acre-feet of water on to the Eastern Snake River Plain and seepage had raised the aquifer and the spring flows. They reached their highest level in the early 1950s. After that the increased use of sprinklers and other water conservation measures began dropping the aquifer and the springs toward their earlier levels.

On the north side of the plain, the Big Lost and Little Lost rivers disappear into the porous lava of the desert floor to feed the aquifer. Some experts estimate that water flowing from the aquifer today at Thousand Springs fell as rain and snow during the Civil War. The aquifer, which changes little from year to year, provides some ballast to the annually fluctuating flows of the Snake River. Together, the two water sources, inextricably connected, form the water resource that today supplies drinking water to nearly a quarter of a million people and irrigation water for nearly four million acres of farm ground.

From one end of a small lake straddling the Continental Divide in the high country of the southern Yellowstone Plateau, water flows toward the Yellowstone River, the Missouri, the Mississippi and eventually the Gulf of Mexico. From the other end of the lake, water flows to the Pacific Ocean. Here, at 9,800 feet above sea level, the Snake River is born of snowmelt and spring water. The Snake flows south out of Yellowstone National Park and into Jackson Lake, east of the Grand Teton Mountains. It leaves the lake and continues south, and passing the town of Jackson, it runs down a steep, rocky gorge and empties into what is now Palisades Reservoir. Once released from the confines of that dam in Idaho, it forms the South Fork of the Snake, well known to canoeists and fly fishers in drift boats.

Another fork wells up in the Island Park caldera on the west side of Yellowstone to form the storied Henrys Fork, which joins the South Fork just north of Idaho Falls. Along its way west, the river steadily loses elevation. On its 1,038-mile journey, the Snake River drops about 9,500 feet in elevation from its mountain headwaters in Yellowstone. It flows through Idaho Falls at about 4,500 feet and drops to 3,500 as it passes Twin Falls. By the time it flows south of Boise it has dropped to about 2,500 feet. When it reaches the Columbia River in south-central Washington the Snake has dropped to 340 feet.

Along the way the Snake collects waters from lesser streams flowing down from the hills to the south and from the lava plain to the north, draining more than 100,000 square miles. The Wood River and Clover Creek and a series of springs enter from the north. Tributaries from the south side included Goose Creek and Dry Creek in the east. Rock Creek runs diagonally across the Twin Falls tract. To the west the tributaries from the south include Cedar Draw, Deep Creek and the canyon of Salmon Falls Creek, which marks the western boundary of the Twin Falls tract.

Ten million years ago the Snake's Pliocene ancestor meandered near its present course. Recurring ice ages sent cascading meltwaters down this river, scouring the riverbed, depositing sediments and forming flood plains, according to the U.S. Geological Survey. It worked its way around the shield volcanoes and eventually cut its deep, narrow canyon. Periodic catastrophic floods from at least ten Ice Ages scoured out and enlarged the canyon. The floods also washed minerals, including gold, out of the mountains to be deposited in river gravels.

The most recent of those floods happened eighteen thousand to fifteen thousand years ago. Near the end of the most recent Ice Age, large glaciers in the Wasatch and Sierra Nevada mountains began to melt as the climate warmed. Precipitation increased and water filled the interior basins of Utah, Idaho and Nevada. The largest of these was Lake Bonneville, up to twenty thousand square miles, covering much of northern Utah and extending up into southeastern Idaho and eastern Nevada. The ancient shorelines can still be seen as a narrow bench along the Wasatch Front, on the hillsides high above Salt Lake City and Ogden and the surrounding hills. The lake was 325 miles long, 135 miles wide and more than a thousand feet deep. It was a terminal lake; rivers flowed into it but it had no outlet. With rain and stream flow from rapidly melting glaciers outpacing evaporation, the lake continued to grow. Lake Bonneville finally began to spill over the basin's lowest point at what is now Red Rock Pass in southeastern Idaho. The water quickly eroded the soft rock, enlarging the outlet, and began spilling out of the giant lake at an increasing rate.

The Bonneville Flood unleashed more than three hundred eighty cubic miles of water. It ran north into the Marsh Creek and Portneuf River valleys and entered the Snake River north of present-day Pocatello, where the flood turned west to follow the river across southern Idaho.

From geologic evidence, scientists have estimated the peak flow in the river at thirty-three million cubic feet per second, enough to fill a train of tank cars 165 miles long each second. Water more than three hundred feet deep traveled at 70 mph. The effect was similar to the Lake Missoula floods that carved the Columbia River Gorge through the Cascade Mountains. Geologists say these peak flows lasted less than a month, but high flows of roiling water continued for more than a year.

The Snake River channel was too narrow and too shallow to handle that much water and quickly filled. About thirty miles east of Milner Dam, near the present city of Rupert, the deluge split. Part of the flow filled the existing canyon, scouring and widening it, rolling and tumbling house-sized blocks of basalt. The rest of the flow spread into the Rupert Channel and out over the plain north of the river, through what now are the towns of Eden and Hazelton, covering about three hundred square miles with water up to fifty feet deep. The flood scoured the topsoil down to bare basalt, leaving a channeled scabland similar to the country around Grand Coulee in central Washington. The Rupert flow eventually spilled over the north canyon rim to rejoin the river. The turbulence along the north canyon rim tore out thousands of tons of basalt blocks, carving out large alcoves and leaving now-dry cataracts in places known today as Vineyard Lake, Devil's Corral and the Blue Lakes Alcove.

Evidence of the catastrophic flood is left in the rock surfaces polished by water-borne sand. The water tore away weak surface rock, exposing the distinctive layers of basalt and in some places massive outcrops of light gray rhyolite. The most dramatic was Shoshone Falls, where the river drops over a rhyolite ledge more than two hundred feet high and a thousand feet wide. It became known as the Niagara of the West. The falls undoubtedly existed before the flood, but it was forever changed by the raging waters and boulders. In the Snake River Canyon the flood gouged out an estimated fifty billion cubic feet from the Twin Falls area.

When the waters receded, the canyon was revealed much as it looks today, with turbulent rapids, thundering falls and the crystalline blue waters of Vineyard Lake and the Blue Lakes. The empty alcove of Devil's Corral became a haven for nineteenth century horse thieves. The large alcoves and smaller ones like them also provide protective habitats for native wildlife including fox, coyote and mule deer. Paw prints of mink, muskrat and other small mammals, as well as insects and weeds moved by the wind, are left in the soft sand. Willows and Russian olives offer a little ragged shade, and reeds line the banks of spring–fed streams. Orange lichens and dark green mosses decorate huge boulders left scattered by the deluge. A chokecherry clings precariously to a rock outcrop where an alcove drops down to the Snake River level.

Several miles downstream, the river widens. Deposited rocks that look like giant petrified watermelons several feet in diameter, rounded from tumbling along the river bottom, are known simply as "melon gravel." In some places the current deposited huge gravel banks. It was in such a gravel bank that the evidence of the earliest residents along the river was found.

One morning in 1989 during normal operations at a gravel pit near the town of Buhl, just west of the city of Twin Falls, Nellis Burkholder noticed what looked like a bone on the screen separating gravel. Thinking it looked like it might be a human thigh bone, he took it home. His wife showed it to an anthropologist friend at the College of Southern Idaho in Twin Falls. The next day, anthropologist Jim Woods and several others swarmed over the gravel pit to look for more bones. About half of a human skeleton was recovered, including the complete skull and jaw. They had found the remains of a young woman eighteen to twenty years old.

But this was no ordinary skeleton. Burkholder had stumbled onto one of the oldest, most complete skeletons ever found in North America. Tests dated the remains from about twelve thousand years ago, making it the oldest skeleton ever found in Idaho. The woman was nicknamed "Buhla" for the nearby town. She may have been among the ancestors of the Northern Paiute, Western Shoshone, or other American Indian tribes who lived in southern Idaho when the first white settlers arrived. Some scientists estimate that the canyons, hills and lava plains of southern Idaho had been home to humans as early as fifteen thousand years before Europeans arrived here. A few miles east of the Buhl gravel pit, in Wilson Butte Cave, other archeologists found, not bones, but conclusive evidence of early inhabitants that has been dated to about 13,000 B.C.

The land they inhabited was anything but the wasteland described by early European pioneers. The canyons and alcoves in the canyon walls provided sheltered village sites and access to the river. The harsh, remote desert nearby offered solitude for vision quests and other spiritual outings and, later, refuge from the persecution of white settlers. Here the ancient inhabitants hunted deer, antelope, bighorn sheep and other animals year-round. Large complexes of hunting blinds and rock walls were located near major campsites. Some tribes used dogs to herd antelope into corrals. They used traps, nets and clubs for rabbits, birds, rodents and other small game. They broiled or sun dried the meat. Their diet also included caterpillars, larval bees, ants and other insects. They fished for salmon in the river at rapids downstream of Shoshone Falls, Kanaka Rapids and Salmon Falls (also known as Fishing Falls.)

The ancient inhabitants also depended on nutritious starchy bulbs and roots, such as camas, bitterroot, biscuitroot and wild onions. All of them were important food sources. They gathered seeds, mashed and roasted them. They picked, mashed and sun dried chokecherries. They baked camas bulbs and other tubers dug from the earth. In late winter they found fresh green thistle and squaw cabbage around springs. Later in the season they gathered seeds of Idaho fescue, wheatgrass, Indian rice grass, bluegrass, cattail, rushes and sunflowers. They winnowed the seeds in broad flat baskets, ground them into flour and added water to make a mush. They also stored seeds in pits, baskets and caves near their winter villages. Later in the summer, they would gather berries and the bulbs of camas, lily, arrowroot, wild onions and wild carrots in moist areas near springs. As winter approached, with freezing winds and deep, driven snow, they moved to protected villages.

Native plants provided more than just food. The native people made bows from the wood of serviceberry and juniper trees. They carried water in small, tightly woven baskets sealed with pitch. They made baskets from the bark of sagebrush and squawbush bark and branches. From the tough, stringy sagebrush bark they also made blankets, ropes, and sandals. They mixed various plants for poisons and medicines. Squawbush berries could be eaten raw or boiled to make a drink resembling pink lemonade. Coyote willow, which grows thick along streams and rivers in the desert, provided long, flexible shoots that they used to make baskets. The salacin in the willow is related to aspirin, and they used it to treat toothache and stomachache, as well as for diarrhea, dysentery and venereal disease. The leaves of big sagebrush made a tea that these ancient people used for colds, diarrhea and to ward off ticks.

Their probable descendants — Western Shoshone and Northern Piute and Bannock — were slaughtered or herded onto reservations by people who said they found barely enough grass to feed their livestock and described the landscape as a barren, sunblasted wilderness.

On August 29, 1812, Robert Stuart and his east-bound party left their camp at Rock Creek and headed across the sagebrush plain toward the main river to try to recover some of the items Hunt's ill-fated party had cached the previous fall. At Caldron Linn, near the site of the present city of Murtaugh, they found the remains of the wrecked canoe, lodged irretrievably in the rocks about a mile below where Dry Creek joins the river. Farther upstream, about two and a quarter miles below The Cedars, they found Hunt's caches. Most of them had been opened and their contents taken or strewn around. Continuing upstream, they found a long, serious rapid — known to white-water rafters and kayakers today as the Milner Reach or the Milner Gorge. Rising from the river in this rapid, they saw the rock that had spelled doom for Clappine. The rock rose in the middle of a bowl where the river makes a right turn, sending the full force of its water into the bowl and creating a vicious whirlpool.

As Stuart stopped and looked out across the lava plain, he did not see the potential of the fertile volcanic soil. And he hurried on. August is hot in the high sagebrush country of southern Idaho, and New York was a long way away. Stuart's route east, considerably south of the route of Lewis and Clark and Hunt's westward journey, eventually formed the basis of the Oregon Trail. But more important, Stuart's route led him to the South Pass in Wyoming, a low pass across the Continental Divide that was key to the Oregon Trail. From there he headed down the fur traders' highway of the North Platte River.

Following a few years later, other explorers and fur trappers refined the route Stuart had scouted. In 1832, Captain Benjamin Bonneville led a train of wagons over South Pass. But the key to opening that now famous trail came ten years later.

In 1842, sponsored by his father-in-law, Missouri Senator Thomas Hart Benton, Captain John Charles Fremont headed west to map the trail and write the trail guide that helped many pioneers find their way West. Fremont was born in Georgia in 1813, attended Charleston College and taught mathematics. He was commissioned as a second lieutenant in the U.S. Army Corps of Topographical Engineers in 1838. In September 1843, he passed through southern Idaho. He stopped at The Cedars, where he found a sheltered campsite with plenty of wood in country he described as sandy and covered with sagebrush and bunchgrasses. The river was smooth and reached below a sandy slope. But beyond three small islands, the river entered a long, steep-walled canyon. He moved on and camped at Rock Creek, with plenty of swift water and lined with willows. The crossing a few miles downstream was rocky. The stream was about twenty feet wide, with a deep bed and steep banks, it was lined with willows and a little grass. He regained the Snake River at Kanaka Rapids and stopped at Salmon Falls. He crossed the Snake River — with some difficulty — at the Three Island Crossing near present-day Glenns Ferry.

Fremont's detailed notes on the Oregon Trail, with mileage, campsites and terrain, and the maps of German cartographer Charles Preuss, were published in 1845 in seven sections convenient for travelers. The maps became the guide for the Oregon Trail pioneers already streaming west in rising numbers. Most of them pulled their wagons along the routes Fremont mapped. They camped where Fremont, and Stuart before him, had camped by the Snake River and at Rock Creek. Fremont died broke in New York in 1890, but the maps of his expedition brought thousands of people through southern Idaho.

Timing brought most of these Oregon Trail pioneers to southern Idaho in August—the hottest, driest and most inhospitable month. It was a time when most game animals migrated to summer range high in the hills. As a result, the pioneers carried away the impression of a desolate, God-forsaken wasteland. This country was far different from the green farms and forests they had known in the wetter eastern states of home.

Parts of the Oregon Trail remained in use until about the turn of the century as a freight road, and for cattle and sheep drives. Thousands passed through southern Idaho on their way to California and Oregon. Few gave a second thought to the potential of fertile sagebrush soil. No one seriously considered settling here.

Then gold was found.

In the spring of 1860, Elias Pierce discovered gold on the Nez Perce reservation in the Clearwater River drainage in northern Idaho. His discovery was modest, but it touched off the first Idaho gold rush. Others found gold on Orofino Creek, and their success inspired still more men to seek their fortunes in other drainages. Up on the Salmon River, the Florence Basin drew about 10,000 miners by 1862. That same year, gold was discovered in the Boise Basin. Miners learned they could be more successful by working together to dig ditches to sluice water in sufficient quantities to wash away mountainsides. By 1863, Idaho City boasted a population of 6,200 souls, making it the largest city in the Northwest at the time.

New miners continued to arrive. Some found a rich strike at Jordan Creek in the Owyhee Mountains in the southwestern part of the state. The remains of once-proud Silver City, Queen of the Owyhees, still stand as mute reminder of the rich veins in the rocky mountainsides.

In 1863, Boise City was founded on the Oregon Trail to serve as a supply center for the miners in Idaho City and Silver City. Two years later it became the territorial capital. Meanwhile, soldiers from Fort Boise were panning near where the Boise River joins the Snake. The gold they found sent prospectors up the

Snake. The Ice Age floods had washed fine-grained gold out of the mountains of eastern Wyoming and Yellowstone. But the fine gold dust, known as "flour," frustrated their efforts. Not until the "burlap sluice" was invented, some years later, did this fine-grained gold yield good results. The best sites were west of American Falls on Bonanza Bar and along the Snake River from Raft River to the present-day city of Buhl. Mining camps sprang up along the Snake—Dry Town near Murtaugh, Springtown on both sides of the river near the present city of Twin Falls and Mudbarville near Buhl. Some deposits still remain in the river gravels.

A.R. Schultz courtesy U.S.G.S.

Burlap tables trap fine grained "flour" gold dust near McCoy Creek on the Snake River.

The discovery of gold lured thousands to the wilds of Idaho, and the booming population resulted in the establishment of the Idaho Territory. The influx of miners brought the need for supplies. Most of the freight during the 1860s, 1870s and 1880s came to Idaho from Salt Lake City along a wagon road that turned north into Idaho at Kelton, Utah. The Kelton Road brought freight to Boise and supplies for the miners in the Snake River Canyon and mountain valleys to the north. Stagecoaches carried mail and brought prospectors to the Rock Creek area. They also brought a few settlers—people who sought riches other than gold. And they brought the people who would shape the future of southern Idaho.

Courtesy Twin Falls Canal Co.

The townsite of Milner that would be home to the workers who built
Milner Dam from 1903 to 1905.

Chapter Four:
Rock Creek Crossing

Charlie Walgamott loved the West. When he got off the train in Kelton, Utah, in 1874, it was one of the busiest freight depots along the five-year-old intercontinental railroad. In his memoir, *"Six Decades Back,"* he describes the raw-boned western, wind-blown railroad town. American Indians in blankets loitered about. Oxen and mule teams and loaded wagons waited in the streets. Every other door opened into a saloon. He loved the smoky smell of Indian-tanned buckskin, the sagebrush-sweetened atmosphere and the ever present element of risk hanging like a mist over the landscape.

Charles Shirley Walgamott had caught western fever from his sister's frequent visits to the family home in Iowa. She had married a stagecoach driver and gone west. It wasn't long before Charlie just had to go west, too. Walgamott and a friend named John Graber caught the train to Kelton, the terminus of the stage and wagon road to Boise and points west. They stayed only long enough to catch a stagecoach north into Idaho. Walgamott, born September 20, 1856, was not yet eighteen. On August 8, 1874, they arrived at the junction where the Kelton Road and the Oregon Trail met, known as Rock Creek Station, a few miles south of the present city of Twin Falls.

Within the next ten years, Walgamott would take in the man whose vision eventually would transform the sagebrush sea into thriving agricultural lands and communities. Walgamott would befriend many of the local settlers who played key roles, and he would watch the changes they brought to southern Idaho. Walgamott went to work for his brother-in-law, Charles Trotter, driving the stagecoach from Rock Creek to Marsh Basin. Marsh Basin was renamed Albion and became the county seat when Cassia County was created a few years later.

In the 1840s, Trotter and his brother, William, had gone to work as stagecoach drivers in Iowa, where William met and married Walgamott's sister, Irene, the daughter of a casket maker in Birmingham, Iowa. As settlement moved west, the brothers moved with the stage lines. Eventually they went to work for the stagecoach king, Ben Holladay, driving the distinctive red Concord coaches of his Overland Stage Line, which eventually reached from the Mississippi to the Pacific Coast. At the time, Holladay's cross-country stagecoach line was one of the few alternatives to the grueling sea voyage south around Cape Horn or the hazardous trip across the Panama Isthmus.

Both Trotter brothers rose to positions as division managers. But as the transcontinental railroad moved out from the east, the stage lines shortened, and they took jobs on the line from Kelton to The Dalles in Oregon. In 1869, Charles Trotter went to work managing Rock Creek Station. William took over City of Rocks Station, about fifty miles to the south.

The Kelton Road came in from the southeast through the Oakley Valley along Goose Creek. It skirted the foot of the South Hills, heading northwest to Rock Creek Station, where it met the Oregon Trail. For the pioneers on the trail, the camp had served as a watering and rest stop since their wagons had begun rolling through more than thirty years earlier. The trail came over twenty dusty miles from a camp to the northeast on the Snake River at The Cedars. Where the Oregon Trail and Kelton Road met, the creek was a welcome oasis after miles of hot sun and dusty trail. Before the pioneers, the northern Paiute and Shoshone Indians had camped and rested along the cool, clear waters of Rock Creek.

The first permanent presence at Rock Creek was a cabin Ben Holladay built in late 1863 along that route. The cabin was part of a string of way stations he built to service the fast freight and mail route he ran from Salt Lake City through southern Idaho and Boise. The route eventually reached into Oregon, with Holladay's way stations every ten or twelve miles and larger home stations every fifty to fifty-five miles. In March 1864, he won a mail contract from Salt Lake City to Boise and Walla Walla, and later to

The Dalles in Oregon. He completed the buildings and staked out the road in time for the first run to Boise on August 8, 1864.

The Stricker store at Rock Creek Station today.

Rock Creek became one of the home stations on the route. The lava rock structure served as hotel and barn. It could accommodate forty horses and became home to off-duty stage drivers. The station also offered a place where passengers could buy a meal or a night's lodging on the 240-mile, two-day journey from Kelton to Boise. Tired pioneers and travelers often took a few days rest here. Eventually a small community grew up around the home station.

Though still largely unsettled, enough traffic passed through the area on the stagecoach and freight line from Kelton and on the Oregon Trail to inspire James Bascom to build a store at Rock Creek Station in 1865. For many years it was the only trading post between Salt Lake City and Boise. Livestock owners and ranch hands came to depend on the store. The one room, eighteen- by twenty-foot log building still stands.

The Central Pacific and Union Pacific railroads joined with the golden spike driven at Promontory, Utah in 1869. After the completion of the railroad, Kelton, about thirty-five miles west of Promontory, became a main shipping point on the Central Pacific

Railroad, and the Kelton Road became a key transportation link to the Northwest. The railroad cut the stage line that had originated in Salt Lake City, making the dusty, windblown Utah town the southeastern terminus of the wagon road for freight and passengers on their way up through Idaho, to Boise, Walla Walla and The Dalles in Oregon. At its peak between 1869 and 1884, the Kelton Road handled the largest volume of wagon freight of any road in the United States. The road also gained some notoriety. The stagecoaches, carrying riches gleaned from mines in the Wood River Valley and the Snake River Canyon, became easy prey for robbers as they passed through the rough terrain in the remote hills along the border between Utah and Idaho. Holdups were a regular occurrence.

In the years following the completion of the transcontinental railroad, Rock Creek reached the peak of its prosperity. But it was short-lived. When the Oregon Short Line Railroad came through to the north in 1883, traffic on the road quickly declined. Rock Creek and Kelton were left isolated, for most freight wagons were nearly obsolete. Today little is left of Kelton—some old railroad timbers, a few concrete foundations and a cemetery. During the height of railroad construction it had housed up to eight thousand people, many of them Chinese laborers, and most of them in tents.

Meanwhile, in 1876 Bascom had sold the store at Rock Creek to Herman Stricker, who became one of the area's early irrigators. Stricker filed on three hundred miner's inches of water—or six cubic feet per second—from Rock Creek to irrigate fields bordering the creek. In 1884, he filed on another two hundred inches. He built a ditch to divert water onto about 960 acres—one and a half sections. He raised wheat, alfalfa, fruit and vegetables for the local market. In 1879, Lucy Walgamott had come to Idaho to visit brother Charlie and her sister Irene. She met and fell in love with Herman Stricker. The two married in 1882. At the time, Rock Creek Station was the center of settlement, and despite being bypassed by the railroad, it continued to grow. In 1880, the census reported forty-four residents. By 1900, the population had grown to a hundred and forty-six. It would swell even larger in the coming years, during construction of the Twin Falls canal system.

Most people who passed through southern Idaho on the Oregon Trail and the Kelton Road cursed the dust and saw only the vast, seemingly endless tracts of sagebrush. But cattlemen brought their livestock through to sell meat to the miners, and they took notice of the rich grasses in the bottomlands along the creeks. In the early 1870s, ranchers wintered three hundred to four hundred head of cattle in the Goose Creek Mountains on the south side of the Snake River. That quickly grew to three thousand to four thousand head. More followed. Large herds were moved through

Root cellar and one time jail cell in the original Rock Creek Station dates from 1864.

the area to ranches in Wyoming or markets in the east. The railroads had given them access to the larger eastern markets. The ranchers now brought their livestock here to take advantage of the cheap, abundant grasses, no longer to sell meat to miners. Among them were A.J. Harrell's Shoe Sole and Point ranches that reached from central Nevada to the Snake River.

By 1882, about 175,000 head grazed the rangelands south of the Snake in Cassia County between the Bruneau River and Goose Creek. Others grazed in the Raft River valley to the east. The cattlemen drove their stock to the railhead—at the time it was in American Falls—where the animals were loaded onto trains for eastern markets. Others trailed their stock to Wells, Nevada, and shipped by rail to San Francisco. A few were still sold to miners in the Wood River Valley.

Grazing was so intense during the 1870s and 1880s that in the severe winters of 1889 and 1890, with little left to eat, livestock died by the thousands.

Frank Riblett arrived in southern Idaho in 1875. He was the nephew of farmer Jerry Riblett of Pennsylvania, the first postmaster in Oakley. Frank Riblett, born on Christmas Eve in 1854 in Pekin, Illinois, became the first teacher in Marsh Basin's first school, in present-day Albion. He came West for the job. The following year another teacher arrived.

John Frederick Hansen, born in 1854 in Copenhagen, Denmark, had emigrated to Indianapolis, Indiana, with his brother Lawrence, in 1872. John Hansen was educated as a school teacher, but he was troubled with respiratory problems—some sources say it was asthma, others say malaria. The Hansen brothers met two sisters, Marie and Anna Petersen, at a Danish singing society in Indianapolis. Lawrence married Marie in 1874. John Hansen took a liking to Anna. But his health had not improved in Indianapolis, and a letter extolling the healthy climate in the West inspired Hansen to move to Idaho.

In 1876, he took the train to Kelton, Utah. There he boarded a stagecoach for Idaho. He was 22. Plagued by chills and fever, he got off the stage and rested for two days. After recuperating, he finally made it to Rock Creek. He found work on a farm, than tried his hand at placer mining, and in the fall of 1876 he began teaching school at the Oakley Meadows Station on the Kelton Road, one of the earliest schools in the area. He established a homestead on Cottonwood Creek and irrigated his crops and watered his stock with water from the creek.

After a year out West, Hansen became lonely for Anna Peterson, and proposed to her by mail. She accepted. On a hot August day in 1877, she arrived on a Union Pacific train in Kelton—amid dust, cinders and flies—with her sister, Marie Hansen, and her two daughters, Hedvig and Laura. They had spent nine days on the train from Indianapolis, comforted only by the quilts and blankets they had brought. Anna's husband-to-be met them at the station at 6 a.m. Sunburned and his health recovered, he loaded everyone and all their baggage into a wagon for the three-day trip through empty sagebrush grassland to Rock Creek.

At Rock Creek Station, John Hansen had met and befriended Charlie Walgamott. When John and Anna were married on September 2, 1877, Walgamott was the best man. A cabin door was pressed into service as a banquet table to accommodate the guests at the first wedding among white settlers in southern Idaho. The union produced four daughters and one son. Walgamott at the time was engaged to a woman named Lettie Dunn.

Two years later, Hansen took on another job.

In 1879, the Territorial Legislature created Cassia County — everything south of the Snake River and east of Devil Creek to Raft River. Marsh Basin was renamed Albion and became the county seat, and the main stage line was changed to run through Albion. Frank Riblett was elected county surveyor. He borrowed $200 to buy a surveyor's transit, and armed with his own surveyor's compass, he set out to survey the area. He hired fellow teacher Hansen to help him.

Meanwhile, Walgamott stayed on, and in 1879 he married Lettie Dunn. Not content with driving a stagecoach, he set out prospecting in the still-active gold camps in the Snake River Canyon near Springtown, a small tent city of white and Chinese miners. The Chinese often were forced onto the poorest claims, but as whites gave up, the Chinese eventually moved onto most of the claims in the canyon. In the 1870s, an estimated five hundred Chinese miners worked these claims. Supplies came by train to Kelton, then by wagon to Rock Creek, and finally by pack train from there. Walgamott worked claims in the gravel deposits with a partner. He also prospected at Jenny's Flat, across the river from an alcove in the canyon wall with two clear blue lakes. He worked with a man who held the placer mining claim there; like most of the white miners, he soon abandoned his claim.

But things were about to change.

A rail line through southern Idaho had been a Union Pacific dream since 1867, when chief engineer Grenville Dodge scoped out the route. The railroad wanted its own connection to the Pacific, and Union Pacific leaders had approved a route through Idaho and Oregon to the coast in 1868. Union Pacific president Sidney Dillon later took up the idea. He had wanted to connect with the Central Pacific at Kelton to follow the route of the freight road, but the Central Pacific wouldn't go along. Instead, Dillon set the connection in Granger, Wyoming. The line eventually ran from Granger to Huntington, Oregon, where it met with another Union Pacific company building east from Portland.

The Oregon Short Line was incorporated in the Wyoming Territory on April 14, 1881. Construction began with a ceremony on July 11, 1881, at Granger and from there drove steadily across southern Idaho. On August 2, 1882, Congress made it a railroad corporation in the territories of Utah, Idaho and Oregon.

In 1881, Ed P. Coleman from Manhattan, Kansas, went to work for the Union Pacific Railroad in Idaho. Just twenty years old and a graduate of Kansas Agriculture College, he joined an engineering party as a surveyor and was sent to help lay out the route through Idaho. Coleman's survey party was sent out into the sagebrush lands about halfway between the present towns of American Falls and Shoshone. The work consisted of setting stakes to mark the route and the grade for the construction crews that would soon follow. Workers slept in tents and ate well. Coleman's survey crew included two parties, each consisting of a chief, two men, a teamster, team and wagon, plus a cook and another teamster with a four-horse team, whose job was to haul water from the Snake River, a two-day trip.

The rail line ran west out of Pocatello and reached American Falls on June 20, 1882, where it crossed the Snake River. The rail line continued across southern Idaho on the north side of the river. Some of the construction camps along the way became the area's earliest communities. The tracks reached Minidoka on January 13, 1883. In February, construction crews established a camp they called Naples on the Wood River. Track reached the camp in March, one hundred eight miles from Pocatello. The town that grew up around the railroad roundhouse and maintenance shops at Naples was later renamed Shoshone, for the spectacular falls twenty-three miles to the south. Here progress was halted to build a seventy-mile branch line north to the mining district of Hailey in the Wood River Valley.

In 1864, a prospector named Warren Callahan had discovered galena deposits, a combination of lead and silver. Development was slow at first, in part because of the difficulty of the terrain. Things didn't get moving until 1879, when about three thousand prospectors began to spread from Rocky Bar to the Yankee Fork of the Salmon River. David Ketchum built the first cabin in the town then called Leadville—later renamed for him. By the time the railroad arrived in Shoshone, the area had two thousand mines and a growing population. The rush created shortages of most things. Mines, mills and small communities with more tents than buildings scattered throughout the valley.

G.K. Gilbert, courtesy U.S.G.S.

A current-driven ferry takes a party across the Snake River above Shoshone Falls in 1899.

The tracks reached Hailey late in 1883, and crews completed laying track into Ketchum in early 1884. The railroad, making possible a fourteen-hour trip from Salt Lake City, brought mining and milling equipment to the Wood River Valley and hauled out the ore. Until then it had been hauled in wagons. The railroad made mining more profitable, and the delay in progress on the railroad mainline indicated just how important those mines were in the Wood River Valley. Westward progress on the Oregon Short Line resumed in 1884, and it reached Huntington, Oregon, on November 10, where it joined the Oregon Railroad and Navigation Company.

The arrival of the railroad in Shoshone in 1883 marked the beginning of the end for the stagecoaches and the freight lines that plied the Kelton Road. But the railroad also brought the future. When he learned the railroad would be coming to Shoshone, Walgamott surveyed a stagecoach road from Shoshone to land he had claimed on the north side of Shoshone Falls the summer after he arrived. He was taken with the place and imagined a hotel to house the tourists drawn to this dramatic waterfall plunging 212 feet. He had posted squatters notices and built a dugout shack on the north side of the falls. When the railroad arrived, Walgamott and his partner, Joe Sullaway, a stage driver, started running stagecoach tours from Shoshone railroad station to two large tents they had set up at Shoshone Falls as a makeshift hotel. The first three weeks they didn't have a single rider. Eventually business picked up, and to make room for more guests he strung up some hammocks. The hammocks were unpopular at first. But the resourceful Walgamott spread campfire stories about the local rattlesnakes crawling into bed with people.

Charlie eventually sold his interests at Shoshone Falls to Senator W. A. Clark and three others who built a wooden hotel that stood for thirty years overlooking the falls. Despite the humble start, the hotel over the years boasted some high-profile visitors including Homer Pound, father of Ezra Pound; Jay Gould; Teddy Roosevelt before he became president; William Jennings Bryan; Idaho Governor Mason Brayman; Edward R. Harriman, then president of the Union Pacific Railroad, and Harriman's seven-year-old son Averell, who later founded the Sun Valley Resort.

Late one evening in October 1884, there was a knock at the door of Charlie Walgamott's cabin on the north side of Shoshone Falls. Outside stood a young man, about five feet, four inches tall and about 135 pounds, Walgamott recounts in his memoirs. "My name is Bert Perrine," the young man told Walgamott, who invited him inside, where he and his wife, Lettie, fed the young stranger and heard his tale.

Ira Burton Perrine would more than make up for his small stature in the largeness of his vision. Perrine, twenty-three, was the oldest son of eleven children of George W. and Sarah Perrine of Delaware, Indiana, near Muncie. As a boy, the young Perrine had milked a half dozen cows before walking to school every morning. He attended the Morris Hill Academy in Morris Hill and Muscatin College in Muscatin—both in Indiana. One day he wrote a letter to his uncle Arch Lingo, in Bullion, Idaho—one of the mining camps near Hailey—saying he would like to join him in Idaho.

Burt Perrine

Shortly after the railroad had arrived in Shoshone, Perrine stepped off the train at the end of the tracks. He boarded a stagecoach for Bullion and went to work in the Mayflower Mine with Lingo. In a few weeks he had amassed about $100 in savings, when someone stole his money. That's when Perrine decided he wasn't cut out for mining. He worked long enough to buy a small herd of cows. He went to Pocatello and bought twenty dairy cows and drove them back to Bullion with the intention of selling the milk to the miners. With the onset of fall in October, he drove his herd south, looking for a place to winter the cows—someplace warmer than the Wood River Valley, where winter comes early and deep snow lingers far into the spring. In Shoshone, Perrine heard that Walgamott might know of a place where he could winter his cows without having to watch them while he hauled his product to market.

Indeed, Walgamott knew of just such a place. The next day the two drove Perrine's cows west along the canyon rim. From a place known as Emberton Point, they looked down into an alcove with two clear, spring-fed deep blue lakes, three hundred feet below. They made their way down a narrow, twisting trail that led through broken basalt down the otherwise vertical canyon walls. The two spring-fed lakes, about three acres each, sat about two hundred feet above the river. It was perfect. The cove would shelter the cows, and there was plenty of water. Perrine adopted the place. And he and Walgamott remained friends for fifty years.

Bisbee photo No. 520 courtesy Twin Falls Public Library
Perrine's home on the Blue Lakes Alcove

Perrine hauled fruit trees on horseback from the Hagerman valley thirty miles to the west and planted them on what was to become the Blue Lakes Ranch. He planted trees and berries. He dug irrigation ditches and diverted the clear spring water to irrigate the crops. Over time he raised apples, peaches, prunes, pears, plums, cherries, apricots, crab apples, nectarines, quince, persimmons, walnuts, almonds and grapes. He planted mulberries to attract the birds away from the other fruit. The fruit thrived. He sold it in Shoshone and in Bullion. He had twenty kinds of fruit trees, and over time they had taught him the potential of irrigation in this land of plentiful sunshine and water.

Perrine also made friends with a neighboring placer miner in the canyon, and he got involved in placer mining in the canyon himself. Through his neighbor, he became acquainted with a Salt Lake City businessman named Stanley Milner who had several investments in placer operations in the canyon. Perrine established a dairy in Shoshone where he also sold produce from the ranch. It was while attending to business interests there that he met Hortense McKay, daughter of Don McKay, who ran the Lincoln Hotel in Shoshone. The two were married June 5, 1892. He took her to live at the Blue Lakes Ranch.

In the spring of 1889, John Hansen's upstream neighbor on Cottonwood Creek, John Caldwell, dammed the creek, blocking the water Hansen used for his livestock and his crops. Hansen tore out the simple dam. Caldwell filed charges and had Hansen arrested. It may well have been the first water fight in southern Idaho. But the judge did not convict Hansen of anything. Instead he appointed Hansen water master on Goose Creek through the summers of 1889 and 1890.

Hansen already was familiar with the waterways and the lay of the land in Cassia County. For ten years he had worked with Frank Riblett surveying the lands south of the Snake River. In 1887, Riblett had reported on their surveys of arable land along the Snake River. He wrote that a canal could start at Ferry Butte on the Snake River just downstream from the Blackfoot River and run some 250 miles to the Salmon Falls River that today marks the western boundary of the Twin Falls Canal Company. He suggested that such a canal, with a starting point of sufficient elevation, could irrigate all the good lands, as much as 600,000 acres, south of the Snake River and north of the mountains to the south. His survey piqued the interest of private investors. Additional surveys were done by the U.S. Geological Survey in 1889 and 1890 for a federal project at the present-day Minidoka Dam site.

Then in 1890, Idaho became a state; the population of Cassia County at the time was 3,143 people.

The following year, in 1891, Riblett and Hansen asked rancher Edwin A. Jordan to finance a detailed survey of the river and the surrounding lands for a diversion structure and an ambitious irrigation system. Jordan, who owned a ranch near Starrh's Ferry at the mouth of Goose Creek on the Snake, agreed. Hansen and Riblett's calculations showed that about 300,000 acres could be irrigated by gravity flow from a diversion point at The Cedars, a few miles west of where Goose Creek enters the Snake River. Hansen mapped out a canal system with a single, long canal snaking its way generally west along the south side of the river. Riblett and Hansen posted a claim for the water at The Cedars. Jordan presented their plan to Congress. But it went nowhere.

Jordan's efforts to obtain the necessary financing failed. The silver crisis and the resulting international depression in 1893 conspired against them. There was little hope of finding private financing for a project big enough to tame the Snake and to fulfill the potential Riblett and Hansen had seen. Investors were reluctant to put up the large investments needed to build large-scale irrigation projects. Those who had that kind of money were reluctant to risk it with little but the promise of water to secure the investment in such uncertain times.

Also in 1893, the first head of the U.S. Geological Survey, John Wesley Powell, issued his "Report on the Lands of the Arid Regions of the United States." The sober report warned that while there was land enough for lots of settlers, there would not be enough water in the West to irrigate all the suitable lands. The report may have helped discourage investors. Powell argued that large-scale federal help would be necessary to bring irrigation water to dry but otherwise fertile lands. The first attempt by Congress at helping came the following year in the form of the Carey Act—largely ineffectual except in Idaho, and particularly southern Idaho.

Ultimately, like elsewhere in the West, getting water to flow across the arid lands would take money and cooperation. Hansen and Riblett's proposal may have run aground financially, but their ideas and maps did not fade. The ideas eventually would take root in the fertile and visionary mind of I.B. Perrine.

Chapter Five:
The Carey Act

In the early 1880s, a group of settlers in Wyoming trying to build a common irrigation system thought they had found a way around the daunting cost. They formed the Wyoming Development Company in 1883 and sold shares to other settlers to raise the money to build an irrigation system. They all had filed land claims under the Desert Land Act of 1877. But the act allowed entry by individuals, not corporations. Government bureaucrats took that rule literally, and when the individuals appeared to have made entries in the interest of the corporation, the government canceled them. The narrow-minded administration of the act raised the hackles of Wyoming's territorial representative, Joseph Carey, who stepped in to help. He tackled a problem that had kept settlers off much fertile land in the arid west.

In Congress, Carey looked for a way to help farmers get water to those lands. Nowhere were his efforts more successful than in Idaho. Here key legislation that Carey pushed through in 1894 made it possible for men with vision and men with money to connect. Western dreamers enticed empire builders willing to risk money. But the act that carries his name did not live up to Carey's expectations. Except in Idaho and Wyoming, the Carey Act was a failure and a disappointment. The passage of the act had little real effect on settling the arid West. But it had everything to do with the formation of the Twin Falls Canal Company, the largest, most successful privately owned irrigation system in the country.

Born January 19, 1845, in Milton, Delaware, to well established farmer parents, Joseph Carey earned a law degree from the University of Pennsylvania in 1867. He was active politically and worked on General Ulysses S. Grant's presidential campaign. President Grant in return appointed him U.S. District Attorney for Wyoming. He eventually served on the Supreme Court of Wyoming and kept the title of judge the rest of his life. In 1879, tired of public life, he started a ranching and business venture with his brother. His business success, however, pushed him back into the public life, and he was elected mayor of Cheyenne. Subsequently he was elected to represent the Wyoming Territory in Congress.

The early push to irrigate lands in the West was a push to settle the vast, open and all but uninhabited lands. Congress sought to entice settlers with the Homestead Act of 1862 and the Desert Land Act of 1877. The Homestead Act became law in January 1863 and gave would-be farmers 160 acres. The farmer in turn had to live on the land for five years, build a house, dig a well, plow ten acres and fence a part of it. The homesteader could claim another quarter section if he or she planted trees. By 1900, 600,000 farmers settled on eighty million acres under the Homestead Act. But much of the land open to homesteading quickly fell into the hands of railroads, speculators and timber companies, forcing later settlers to buy land from them or settle for second-rate government land, much of it without adequate water.

The Desert Land Act of 1877 handed settlers 640 acres — one square mile. The act required only that the settler bring water to it, which was all but impossible in many locations. Some resorted to filling a tank on a wagon and hauling it out and letting the water run onto the land. In the end, the act benefited mostly cattlemen, by giving them a way to amass large home-ranch property. The unscrupulous paid cowboys to file on lands along streams and turn them over to the rancher, thus securing the best lands for the ranch. In 1891, the amount of land granted was cut to 320 acres. The act also was changed to allow settlers to band together to construct irrigation systems to bring water to the land. But that was still an expensive proposition.

In the arid states, only those lands that could be easily irrigated by the efforts of individual homesteaders were settled early. Large tracts of potentially arable land still were available, but few individual farmers had the money or the expertise to build the irrigation works required to get the water to the land. Until 1891, neither of the acts allowed any way for farmers to cooperate in their efforts or to secure the necessary capital. Even after 1891, the Homestead Act and the Desert Land Act made land available, but neither one included a mechanism or incentive for investors to provide the financial help that was needed to irrigate that land in any meaningful, large-scale way.

The Desert Land Act encouraged the irrigation of arid lands, Carey acknowledged. But he complained that the way the act was administered—each administration making new rules and decisions—made it ineffective, as in the case of the Wyoming Development Company. Development was undermined by interpretations of policy, which defeated the purposes of the act, he said. Carey saw clearly that under the best of circumstances, the irrigation works necessary to bring dry lands under cultivation would be impossible without farmers working together, or without some way of raising money or enticing investors.

"Successful reclamation of desert lands to any general beneficial extent was and is impossible, without expenditure of vast capital and aggregation of individual effort," he wrote. Until better legislation could be passed to promote the irrigation, development and settlement of arid lands, Carey encouraged the government to administer the Desert Land Act in a way that would "encourage the individual and the association of individuals to undertake the reclamation and settlement of the arid lands of the United States."

With the economic collapse of the silver panic in 1883, Carey saw that the U.S. Treasury would be in no position to be of much help for several years to come. As territorial representative, Carey urged Congress to add an amendment to an appropriations bill that would grant two million acres of arid lands to each state on condition it be developed—that is irrigated and cultivated and settled in small tracts. But others encouraged him to withdraw the provision to avoid potential controversy delaying the admission of Wyoming as a state. He agreed. Carey proceeded to write the legislation that admitted Wyoming to the Union as the 44th state on July 10, 1890. He was promptly elected the first senator from Wyoming on November 12, 1890.

When now-Senator Carey returned to Congress, he renewed his effort to get his provision enacted. But not without some opposition. Some western developers—engineers, lawyers, real estate agents—urged the government to simply cede arid lands to the states. But Congress balked.

Carey's ideas weren't new. In the 1860s, William N. Byers, the editor and publisher of the Rocky Mountain News in Colorado, began pushing for federal help to develop irrigation in the arid West, and he urged Congress to pass legislation to provide the means.

"It is a well known [sic] fact to all who are familiar with the country and its climate, that more than one half of the total area of the United States cannot produce crops or grain or vegetables with certainty except by irrigation," Byers wrote in a December 1864 editorial. He professed surprise that Congress hadn't already acted. He proposed the government grant public lands to individuals or companies who would build irrigation diversions and canals. Such a proposal, he argued, would increase the value of the surrounding lands. It would create a market for millions of acres of otherwise unproductive land, and it would promote the growth and economies of western states.

Byers was a man before his time. A bill that would have accomplished much of what he suggested was introduced in Congress but died in committee.

In the late 1880s and 1890s, with most of the easily reached land already irrigated, the states began to get interested. In 1887, California passed the Wright Act, which allowed the formation of irrigation districts to own water in common and sell bonds to finance the construction of diversion works and canals. In Idaho in the early 1890s, *Caldwell Tribune* co-owner Frank Steunenberg, who would later become governor of Idaho, endorsed a proposal to establish state irrigation laws, including a state engineer's office. The Idaho Legislature passed a bill similar to his proposal, but it was vetoed. Steunenberg sold the paper in 1893. New owner Rees Davis pushed a plan similar to California's Wright Act that called for the federal government to cede land to the states for development. The states then would sell construction bonds. But Idaho balked at accepting financial responsibility for irrigation projects.

Carey hadn't given up. In July 1894, he offered two amendments to the Sundry Civil Appropriations Bill. Carey's amendments included the proposals he had withdrawn earlier. The federal government would supply the land, and the state would supervise the construction of irrigation works, canals and ditches, paid for ultimately by the farmers who would settle and farm the land. The act granted one million acres of federal desert lands to each state that chose to participate. The state would contract with a construction company to build the irrigation works, if the company could show sufficient water was available. The details of the irrigation project—the amount of land, the amount of water and any other requirements—would be set out in the contract with the state. Farmers would be allowed to buy parcels as small as forty acres and up to 160 acres from the state at fifty cents an acre, and they would pay their share of the cost to build the diversion and distribution works.

Critics argued that water in arid lands was too precious to be left in private hands. It should remain a public resource. Skeptics warned that irrigation systems built by capitalists would last only long enough to collect from the farmers to recoup the cost of construction—plus a handsome profit.

The measure became law as a rider to the appropriations bill on August 18, 1894. Simply put, participating states would function as the construction contractor for the irrigation works. Few states were in the legal or financial position to do that. Though the law allowed states to contract with others to do the work, few investors were willing to risk capital without adequate protection. In 1896, Congress amended the act to allow the states to create a lien against the land to cover the cost of construction. The states would hold the land in trust until construction was complete and the land developed. The subsequent irrigation and cultivation of the land would pay it back. Farmers had ten years to pay off the land.

The construction company in turn would raise the money to pay for construction by mortgaging the land, issuing bonds or contracting with settlers to buy water rights. When completed and approved by the state, the project would be turned over to an operating company comprised of the farmers who owned the land. The amount of water available, the sale of water rights and the mechanism for turning the project over to the settlers were set out in a contract. After signing the contract with the state, the construction company had three years to start construction. The land would be patented to the settlers when the project was completed and the land was irrigated, cultivated and occupied, all within ten years. Carey had high hopes for the future of the arid lands as a result of the legislation. "It will build up great agricultural districts, indirectly, it will develop great water powers, and cause the erection of manufacturing establishments, and the founding of prosperous American towns and cities," Carey told the *Salt Lake Telegram* in 1894. He was wrong. But the problem was not so much with the act, as with the sketchy information available about water supplies. Most projects under the act failed because the developers either underestimated the construction costs or overestimated the amount of water actually available—or both. Most projects, on average, wound up costing about twice the initial estimates. Inadequate financing and water supplies were not the fault of the act, but the result of poor planning and lack of accurate information, says Mikel H. Williams in his 1970 report, "The History of Development and Current Status of the Carey Act in Idaho."

In addition to poor design and planning, some projects were victims of blatant dishonesty, says Hugh Loving in the Fall 1986 issue of *Idaho Yesteryear*. The act encouraged land speculation, he wrote. Failures also could be blamed on mismanagement by state officials and greedy entrepreneurs. Some openly bilked settlers and investors, he said.

After the act was passed, twelve western states enacted laws that allowed them to participate: Arizona, California, Colorado, Idaho, Montana, Nevada, New Mexico, Oregon, South Dakota, Utah, Wyoming and Washington. Under the act, applications for projects covering 8.4 million acres were submitted; projects on 3.8 million acres were approved. After eight years, only four of the eligible states had applied for land covering 670,000 acres. By 1958, patents had been handed over for just over one million acres—almost two-thirds of that was in Idaho.

In Carey's home state of Wyoming, applications covered almost half a million acres, but only two hundred thousand acres were patented. In Idaho, the applications totaled about three million acres. As in other states, most of the proposed projects were long on vision and short on know-how, water and financing. Only 618,000 acres were eventually patented.

The first of sixty-four projects proposed in Idaho was filed in 1895 on the American Falls project. Work started almost immediately on the Aberdeen-Springfield Canal. The segregation of 57,242 acres was approved in 1899. In 1901 the state and the American Falls Canal and Power Company signed a construction contract for the project. It was completed in 1910 and turned over to the operating company, known as the Aberdeen-Springfield Canal Company. The system included eighty-six miles of main canal and fifty-four miles of laterals, and eventually 50,498 acres were patented. But economic troubles plagued the project.

The American Falls Canal Securities Company took over, and the cost of water rose from the originally projected $10 to $40 per acre. Even so, there was not enough water. The company arranged an agreement with the U.S. Bureau of Reclamation to buy surplus water from the Jackson Reservoir.

Eventually, of the sixty-four projects proposed, twenty-three succeeded. The largest would be the Twin Falls South Side Project, at just over 200,000 acres. The second largest was across the river, the North Side Project, at about 170,000 acres. The Twin Falls project was the largest irrigation development attempted in the country at the time, and the Twin Falls Canal Company became a national showcase for Carey Act projects.

Carey served as U.S. senator until March 3, 1895, and returned to Wyoming, where he served as governor from 1911-1915. He died February 5, 1924, in Cheyenne. He lived long enough to see the shortcomings and the few successes of irrigation projects under the act.

Idaho adopted a law enabling Carey Act participation in 1895, despite opposition. It was amended in 1897 and 1899 before it became workable in the state. The act required a person or company to submit a proposal with a deposit of $250 in a certified check to the state reclamation engineer. The developers could ask for a temporary withdrawal of the land to give them time to complete plans without fear of another, competing project filing on the same land and water. Or the developers, if plans were ready, could apply for a permanent "segregation" of land. The application also had to be accompanied by a permit application to appropriate water if a water right had not yet been established.

The reclamation engineer and the state Land Board had to approve the project before a construction contract could be signed between the state and the company. The engineer would determine whether the project seemed feasible and whether sufficient water was available to irrigate the amount of land covered in the project. Typically, engineers figured one cubic foot per second would be enough to irrigate eighty acres. Many Carey Act projects failed because water supplies were overestimated, and the actual amount was enough to irrigate only a fraction of the land included in the project. To protect itself, the state law did not guarantee the success of a project just because it had been approved.

The state Land Board set the price the construction company could charge for the water in accordance with the cost of building the diversion and delivery systems. The cost ranged from $10 to $65 per acre for the water. The state charged fifty cents per acre for the land. Farmers would pay the state twenty-five cents per acre when they applied for the land and another twenty-five cents per acre when they offered the final proof to patent the land. The settler would pay the construction company separately for the water. But first the transfer must be approved by the state.

The construction company would not own any water rights or the irrigation system. The company was allowed to sell water rights only as a way to recover the cost of construction—plus a reasonable profit—divided among the number of acres irrigated. Each farmer would then pay that cost times the number of acres he would irrigate. The company held a lien on the land and the water right until it was paid. In case of default, the land and water right could be auctioned. The company, however, would be allowed to bid only the amount it was owed.

Farmers got involved in the construction of the project in a number of ways. Some bought stock in the construction company or bonds issued by the company. Some hired on to work on construction crews, while waiting for the water to arrive. Tracts were selected in a variety of ways: by lottery or first come first served, or by buying the water right for a specific tract. To qualify, a farmer had to be a citizen or show intent to become a citizen. State land officials and married women could not apply for land. Veterans were given preference, including married women veterans. The would-be irrigators had to swear that they intended to irrigate, cultivate and settle the land.

Once the system was turned over to them, the farmers could form an operating company to run and maintain the system, and charge an annual assessment to cover operating costs. The company would own the water right, not the individual farmers. That meant there was no priority among users within a project. All had a right to share in the available water based on the number of acres they owned.

The dismal success rate of projects initiated under the Carey Act played a part in congressional approval of arguably the country's most successful irrigation legislation. The National Reclamation Act was passed in 1902, the year before construction got started on the Twin Falls project. In most areas, large-scale irrigation remained unavailable until the Reclamation Act got the federal government involved to plan, design, build, operate and pay for projects in seventeen states. Some suggest that the chronic failure of Carey Act projects led to the 1902 act.

In 1901, Nevada Representative Francis Newland proposed that the government sell arid federal lands suitable for irrigation and put the money into a water development fund. Farmers would be allowed to buy eighty acres at a rate per acre proportional to the cost to build the irrigation works, not unlike the Carey Act. The system would be independent of the congressional purse strings that so many Westerners resented, even back in those days.

Critics of Newland's proposal argued that adding more agricultural lands would compete with existing farms. Some questioned the public benefit of the government promoting private agricultural growth. Some maintained that the same crops could be raised cheaper on existing nonirrigated farms. And no one was sure just how many farmers were ready to move west to farm in the desert. Lots of effort went into marketing irrigated agriculture as superior to agriculture dependent on natural rainfall.

Western lawmakers supported Newland's bill and it passed in

June 1902 as the National Reclamation Act. In the process, Congress raised the limit on the amount of land an individual could buy to 160 acres. On June 17, 1902, President Theodore Roosevelt signed the Newland Act into law. But the idea that irrigation developments would pay for themselves never worked. A substantial portion of the costs of most projects was written off as recreation or flood control benefits and paid by the government. The federal government also failed to enforce the size limit. Instead, the act effectively brought federal tax dollars into the business of building large-scale irrigation projects.

The act also established the Reclamation Service, later renamed the Bureau of Reclamation. The bureau spent $8 billion to irrigate eleven million acres. The agency built 327 reservoirs, fifteen thousand miles of canals and fifty-eight hydroelectric projects. Today it delivers thirty million acre-feet of irrigation water per year. In southern Idaho, the Reclamation Act brought the development of federal Snake River storage reservoirs, known as the Minidoka Project, with a total storage capacity of more than four million acre-feet. The project eventually supplied irrigation water to 1.5 million acres.

Federal reservoirs put control of the river in the hands of the federal government. In return, irrigators got a more dependable water supply. Some resisted the development, and some still resist federal control of water—displaying a proprietary attitude over what is in fact a public resource. In Idaho, theoretically, the people of the state own the water resource. Though many irrigators act as if they own the water, they own only the right to put some of it to beneficial use.

Before the Reclamation Act opened the public purse, irrigators had been on their own. The size and success of the irrigation systems they built were limited only by the amount of financing they could secure. It turned out that was not very much. In the aftermath of the 1893 depression, however, the Carey Act had created a mechanism to link private investors with the land that had potential—a free-enterprise alternative to federal control. The act made it more attractive for private investors to get involved in building irrigation systems—if the land were suitable, the water were available and the system could be built cheaply. All three of those criteria became evident in southern Idaho. The land most likely would have been irrigated even without the Carey Act. But here, the act allowed the irrigation system and lands to remain and thrive in private hands.

"The results attained have been the best and its future value to the state to which it is applicable, is beyond estimation," Senator Carey predicted. Though it did not hold up in most of the West, his prediction certainly came true in southern Idaho.

Bisbee photo A-2 courtesy Twin Falls Public Library

American Falls power plant.

Part Two: The Water

The Snake River Canyon west of Twin Falls.

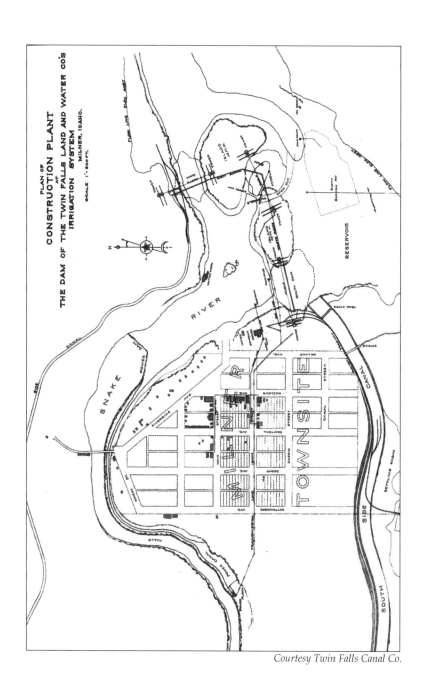

Courtesy Twin Falls Canal Co.

Chapter Six:
Building the Company

During the early 1890s, Burt Perrine's thoughts were on business. The Blue Lakes Ranch thrived, and he raised award-winning produce. He loaded his wagon and hauled it to market in the small towns of the region. One was Marsh Basin, now Albion. On his way, he followed a trail from the ranch along the north side of the river and stopped to rest at The Cedars. Sometimes he camped there. And on his trips, he had plenty of time to ponder the potential of the land.

A few miles east of The Cedars, Perrine crossed the river at Starrh's Ferry at the mouth of Goose Creek about four miles west of present-day Burley. George Starrh built the ferry in 1880 to serve the freight wagons heading from the railroad depot at Kelton, Utah, to the mines in the Wood River Valley to the north. It was not always dependable. Some days up to fifty wagons would be lined up waiting to cross. And some days the wind would counteract the current that drove the ferry across, keeping the ferry idle for three or four days at a stretch. After the railroad arrived on the north side of the river in 1883, freight wagons no longer crossed the river at Starrh's. But for local residents, the ferry still was the only way across. Cattle and sheep ranchers still brought their stock across on the ferry to reach the railhead at Kimama. Other local traffic, like Perrine, used the ferry until the railroad was built along the south side of the river in 1905. For them, it was the easiest place to cross the river at the time.

Once across, Perrine started up the long hill to Albion, to sell his fresh strawberries at the Albion Normal School. Here, in the mid-1890s, he encountered John Hansen, who had been named superintendent of schools in Cassia County and moved his family to Albion in 1892. Eventually the talk turned to irrigation, and the surveys that Hansen had done with Frank Riblett, who also taught school in Albion. Hansen and Riblett had calculated that more than 250,000 acres could be irrigated with water from the Snake River if a dam could be built at The Cedars. Their map showed the largest irrigation proposal of its kind at the time, larger than anything else like it attempted anywhere.

Courtesy U.S.G.S.

I. B. Perrine built his homestead by two spring-fed lakes in the Snake River Canyon, 1903.

Hansen described the way the gently rolling landscape sloped toward the west and toward the Snake River. Above The Cedars, the river was close enough to the surface of the plain that a dam could raise the river enough to divert water along the south side. A canal would take water to the west and south and then west again for many miles. From such a canal, gravity would move the water across the fertile lands to drain into the river. It looked like a perfect system — plenty of water, fertile lands and natural drainage.

The passage of the Carey Act in the summer of 1894 provided some security for investors in such a project. Already in 1895, farmers in the American Falls area a few miles to the east had formed an irrigation company and filed an application for a project that eventually would irrigate more than fifty thousand acres. Work had started on the Aberdeen-Springfield Canal and was progressing well. At the time, no one knew the project would run into financial trouble before it finally was completed.

What Hansen and Riblett had seen, and Perrine quickly grasped, was the potential of the ample waters of the Snake River diverted onto the lands on both sides of the river. They saw farmers tilling fertile fields on thousands of irrigated acres. They saw the Carey Act as a way to overcome the financial obstacle that had thwarted the earlier proposal. Perrine didn't originate the idea, but his persistence and enthusiasm made it possible. He assembled political support, and he convinced businessmen and eastern financiers to put up the serious financial backing needed to build the dam that would tame the river and the canals that would spread its water across the land.

Across the country, the late nineteenth century was a time of industrial fervor. Mark Twain dubbed the era the Gilded Age for its cynical façade of genteel splendor, of emptiness and materialism, of tarnish under a golden patina. The era spanned from the 1870s into early twentieth century and was a legacy of post-Civil War growth. The country was coming of age. Railroads stretched their steel tendrils across the wide plains of the country's midsection. And it was a time of greed and self-importance, when men would let nothing stand in their way to amass wealth. Rich men accumulated large swaths of public land, by means legal and not, including millions of acres of valuable timber lands and other public assets. They earned the title of robber barons, for the empires they built by turning vast public assets into private wealth. Industrialism ruled. The prevailing thought held that the shortcomings of nature could be alleviated with technology, that any problems could be surmounted by engineering.

The Twin Falls canal system was a child of that era. Turning a river into an industrial engine was considered an improvement on nature. The arid lands were thought wastelands, therefore irrigating the desert to create productive farmland was an improvement. In 1885, then-Union Pacific president Charles F. Adams, while touring the recently completed Oregon Short Line, noted that much of southern Idaho required irrigation to realize its potential.

Some who passed through cursed the lack of water. But Perrine and others saw it as a blessing. The waters of the Snake River, gathered as snow in distant mountains and harnessed by irrigation systems, would make agriculture more dependable than in other places where farmers had to rely on natural rainfall. Many thought irrigation would bring arid lands to a level of prosperity unmatched anywhere in the country.

Perrine already knew the value of irrigation firsthand from his success at the Blue Lakes Ranch. His long trips to market gave him plenty of time to think and visually survey the landscape. He would often camp at The Cedars on his regular trips to Albion. He became convinced the two surveyors were right, that the desert could be irrigated on a large scale with water from the Snake River. He tried to get his friend Robert M. McCollum, publisher and editor of the *Shoshone Journal*, to go in with him, to post notices claiming the water in the river at The Cedars. McCollum was intrigued by Perrine's idea of damming the Snake and irrigating the desert. But when the two visited The Cedars, McCollum looked at the raging current and, awed by the physical forces of the rushing river, backed down. Surely, no one could tame that torrent. He refused to pay half of the $2 filing fee for the water rights.

Perrine wasn't one to give up easily. When his friend McCollum wouldn't join him, Perrine paid the filing fee himself. For more serious financial backing, he turned to a businessman from Salt Lake City whom he knew from his own placer mining operation in the Snake River Canyon. Stanley B. Milner, born in Wisconsin in 1850, had moved to Salt Lake City in 1889 and invested in several iron, coal and gold mining operations including placer operations in the Snake River Canyon. He headed the Milner Corporation with his wife, Truth, and their three sons. Perrine visited Milner in his Salt Lake City office to try to interest him in the irrigation project. He showed Milner the map Hansen had given him and told Milner what he had learned from the two surveyors. He invited Milner to visit the Blue Lakes Ranch. The map piqued Milner's interest, and he agreed to come to Idaho and look over the project.

But before Perrine's project even got started, a proposal for a national park nearly derailed it. In August 1898, U.S. Senator

George Shoup of Idaho introduced a proposal for a Snake River Canyon National Park Reserve that would include Twin Falls, Shoshone Falls and the Blue Lakes in the Snake River Canyon and some of the surrounding lands. The U.S. Park Commission became interested and withdrew all lands within the proposal while the project was under study. The proposed park preserve would ban hunting, and limit fishing, grazing and mining. It would block the use of any water that would diminish the scenic beauty of the natural waterfalls. That meant no irrigation, no hydropower, no sprawling canal system.

But Perrine did not sit idle. He convinced Milner to put up $30,000 for a survey. Milner agreed and brought in three key men to launch the Twin Falls Land and Water Company—Salt Lake City investment banker Frank Knox, Boise-area irrigation promoter James Harrison Lowell and Caldwell editor and banker Albert Keppel Steunenberg. Lowell and Steunenberg already were aware of the potential of diverting the Snake River for irrigation. Lowell, born in

Stanley Milner

New Bedford, Massachusetts, in May 1860, had been involved in irrigation projects in California. He had moved to Boise in 1893 and worked as head of the Boise Land and Water Company. He spearheaded the effort to build the reservoir now known as Lake Lowell. Steunenberg moved to Idaho from Knoxville, Iowa. He took over the Caldwell newspaper and established the Commercial Bank of Caldwell. His brother Frank joined him to help with the troubled Caldwell newspaper. Knox had moved to Salt Lake City from Iowa in 1889 and opened the Bank of the Republic in 1890. He had invested in mining properties owned by Milner.

Together, these men formed the Twin Falls Land and Water Company. With their financial backing, on June 25, 1900, Perrine staked claims for three thousand cubic feet per second of water on both sides of the river at The Cedars. The company was formally incorporated on September 3, 1900. Milner, Lowell and Steunenberg each put in $1,000 for one thousand shares. Frank Knox bought ten shares. Perrine put in his water right, his preliminary work and his enthusiasm. The company offices were in Salt Lake City with an Idaho office at Lowell's home in Roswell.

On October 11, 1900, Perrine restaked his earlier water right claims at The Cedars on behalf of the company—in the same place and amount as his claim in June. Perrine also had the support from Idaho Governor Frank Steunenberg, who secured approval from the state Land Board for an initial 248,667 acre project under the Carey Act on October 12. Approval of the formal application for a temporary withdrawal allowed detailed surveys and complete project plans and contracts to be drawn up as required by the state. With a temporary withdrawal in place, others could not apply for the same land or the same water until the withdrawal expired or the project was completed or cancelled.

Meanwhile, the pending park proposal still tied up the land. But with strong local opposition, the proposal was defeated in Congress. On July 1, 1901, the lands that had been under consideration for the park were released by the federal government. That same day, the government approved the temporary withdrawal of 270,000 acres—most of it on the south side of the river and some on the north side—and surveys were to begin immediately. The state appointed its own engineers, A.J. Wiley and State Engineer D.W. Ross—head of what later became the Department of Water Resources.

But Milner didn't trust the Idaho survey crew leaders. He appointed Walter George Filer, one of his own managers, to keep an eye on the Idaho engineers. Filer had come west in 1895 to work as a mining engineer in Helena, Montana. He was born in January 1870 in Sharon, Pennsylvania, and graduated in civil engineering from the Hasbrouck Institute in Jersey City, New Jersey, with classmate Mark M. Murtaugh. Filer worked building railroads in New York and New Jersey before he came west. In 1899 he went to work for Stanley Milner's mining enterprises in Salt Lake City, Utah, running the Annie Laurie Mine. When Milner put him in charge of the Twin Falls project, Filer brought along Murtaugh as his assistant manager. Murtaugh also had worked as a railroad engineer and as an assistant engineer for the Oregon Short Line until he went to work for Filer on the Twin Falls project.

No sooner had they set up their transits and started on the survey, however, than they ran into another delay.

Once the park proposal was dropped in July 1901, releasing the land in the canyon to development, the owners of the hotel at Shoshone Falls filed for an injunction against the Harry L. Hollister Corporation aimed at halting work on a hydroelectric plant at the foot of the falls. Senator William A. Clark of Montana and E.L. Stone, John A. Creighton and Sarah Dewey of Nebraska, had bought the hotel from Charlie Walgamott. With the land and water released for development, however, they were worried that the water diverted through the hydroelectric plant would diminish the scenic beauty of the falls that attracted patrons to their hotel.

Courtesy Twin Falls Canal Co.
Stagecoach crosses the bridge over the Snake River from Perrine's Blue Lakes Ranch.

The injunction covered anything that might diminish the river flow over the falls, including Perrine's upstream water rights. It further delayed the project and led to a rift among stockholders, whose investments in the project had grown in the meantime. Perrine had his hand in this hydroelectric enterprise as well. He had worked for five years on the power plant project with Harry L. Hollister, a Chicago realtor who later helped Perrine promote the Twin Falls irrigation project. Once the park proposal went away,

Hollister and New York financier William Dowe filed on the water right for the power plant at the falls and began work on the project. Then in February 1902, Hollister filed his own suit against the hotel owners at Shoshone Falls. Hollister sought to condemn a little over two and a half acres on the north side of the Snake River to develop the hydropower project that would generate electricity from the falls' 212-foot vertical drop. The court battle over Hollister's project grew bitter and complex. The hotel owners sought unsuccessfully to have the case heard in federal court, because the parties all were from other states. The case went to trial in May 1902. A jury of Lincoln County residents ruled in Hollister's favor and lifted the injunction. At the time, Lincoln County comprised all the land on the north side of the Snake River.

The fight over Hollister's power plant eventually wound up in the state Supreme Court, which reheard the case in 1904. Hollister won the right to build the plant. The state and the hotel owners were awarded $500 each in damages, far less than they claimed the property was worth. Hollister and his backers eventually tunneled through 410 feet of rock, built a powerhouse near the foot of the falls and began churning out power in 1907.

As soon as the injunction was lifted in May of 1902, however, the restraints on Perrine's other water right at The Cedars were removed and work could begin on the irrigation project. Filer started the surveys for the construction camp, which would become the town of Milner. Work also began on a suspension bridge across the river below the dam site.

The rift that had started with the legal tussle and economic strain grew wider. In July 1902, Lowell and Albert Steunenberg, lacking money to continue, wanted the project turned over to the state or federal reclamation, a fate all too familiar across the west at many other Carey Act projects. Together Lowell and Steunenberg had amassed 49,995 shares. Milner controlled 39,995 shares, and Perrine controlled 10,000, resulting in a tie: Milner and Perrine wanted to proceed with the project. Frank Knox still had his ten shares and sided with Perrine and Milner, keeping the project in private hands. Lowell and Steunenberg sold out to Milner.

With the legal hurdles overcome and the land and water right no longer in question, the project still needed serious financial backing. Milner estimated the project would cost about $1.5 million. But the first attempts to find investors were discouraging. The earlier failures of Carey Act projects began to make investors reluctant. Perrine offered a Salt Lake mining broker known as Witcher Jones a commission if Jones could find someone willing to come up with that kind of money. But the key to unlocking the puzzle turned out to be Filer.

Frank Buhl

One of Filer's former associates from his younger days in Sharon, Pennsylvania, was industrialist Frank Henry Buhl, who owned a steel mill in Sharon and was an investor in iron mines owned by Jones. Filer learned from Jones that Buhl happened to be on his way west to look over some promising mining property. By the time Buhl arrived in Salt Lake City, the mine had sold, so Buhl asked Jones if he had any other investment possibilities. Buhl was thinking of mining, but Jones had another idea.

Buhl, born August 3, 1848, was the son of Detroit's first mayor, Christian H. Buhl and his wife, Caroline. Frank Buhl got a thorough education in business. His earliest investments included the Sharon Iron Mills in Pennsylvania. His interests spread into mining and related industries. His successful investments financed his philanthropy. He earned a reputation for his grants to hospitals and schools for needy children and later for war orphans. In 1902 he was worth an estimated $25 million.

When Buhl arrived in Salt Lake City in November 1902, Jones recalled Perrine's enthusiasm for the irrigation project. He and Filer sketched it out for Buhl, who had nothing better to do during the three days before his return trip. Buhl agreed to go up to Idaho and have a look. Perrine arranged a tour, with fresh horses ready along the route. Buhl and his wife, Julia, and Stanley and Truth Milner, Jones, and Filer arrived at the Shoshone station on November 24, 1902. Perrine met them with a wagon and drove them to The Cedars to show Buhl the dam site. They covered many miles of dusty sagebrush country that day. They spent the night at Perrine's Blue Lakes Ranch, where Perrine showed Buhl what the ample water, fertile soil and Idaho sun could do. The next day, after touring the area some more, Buhl praised Mrs. Perrine's hospitality, the beauty of Blue Lakes and Shoshone Falls. But he said nothing about the project and returned east in his private railroad car.

Buhl had seen the potential, however, and was infected by Perrine's enthusiasm. He became convinced that the project would be feasible if it could meet the legal conditions of the Carey Act. He agreed to underwrite it. In early December, Milner, Perrine, Buhl and Filer closed the deal; Buhl agreed to provide $1.5 million. The final surveys and plans were completed in December 1902. And on January 2, 1903, the state Land Board and the Twin Falls Land and Water Company signed a contract for the construction of the dam and canal system under the state law accommodating the Carey Act. After signing the contract the company had three years to complete construction.

Plans included irrigating 240,000 acres of Carey Act land south of the river and west of Milner Dam, and about 32,000 acres north of the river. The south side canal would be sixty-five miles long, and initially capable of carrying three thousand cubic feet of water per second. The canal would be eighty feet wide and gradually narrow to sixty feet by the time it reached the Rock Creek crossing. Along the way the canal would connect to ever smaller canals ending in laterals about two feet wide and one foot deep, capable of carrying enough water for about eighty acres. The contract included details and specifications of the dam, as well as the canal system capacity, rights of way, water rights and land entries, and it spelled out the duties of the Twin Falls Land and Water Company to complete and transfer the system to the farmers.

On January 14, 1903, the Twin Falls Land and Water Company was reorganized, and offices were established in the Atlas Building in Salt Lake City. Milner transferred 62,500 shares to Buhl, leaving Milner with 27,490 shares and Buhl with 65,000 shares. Buhl turned 10,000 shares over to Filer. Perrine sold his remaining 10,000 shares to Milner. And Frank Knox hung onto his ten shares. The reorganization left Buhl as president, with 52.5 percent of the stock and control of the company. Milner had 37.49 percent and was a vice president. Filer, who was vice president and general manager, had 10 percent.

Everything was ready for work to begin.

Then on February 11, 1903, just when things seemed to be on track, the Atlas Building caught fire, destroying all the company's data, including all the surveys, field notes, maps, plats and other papers. The clock was ticking on the construction deadline. Filer had less than three years to complete the dam and canal system.

Courtesy Twin Falls Canal Co.

Survey crew on the Twin Falls Tract in 1903.

Chapter Seven:
Building the Dam

After the February fire, project manager Walter Filer pushed ahead. The company was anxious to show progress, to show skeptical farmers something other than surveys, sagebrush and promises of water. The first visible sign of progress was the suspension bridge across the Snake River just below the dam site at The Cedars, completed later that month. And work on the dam and canals soon got under way. Filer had hired Paul S. A. Bickel as his chief engineer for the Twin Falls project. He had worked with him in Montana. The Twin Falls Land and Water Company hired the construction company Faris and Kesl of Boise to build the dam. The contract for the first twenty-five miles of canal went to Nelson Bennett Company of Tacoma, Washington. Despite the setbacks resulting from the fire, construction began in early March, less than a month later.

Dam construction was a monumental undertaking that forever changed the face of the desert. The entire project covered about four hundred square miles. The main canal was designed to hold four thousand cubic feet per second, a little more than needed. The two-thousand-foot-long rock- and earth-fill dam consisted of three dams in the channels between the two islands and the north and south banks. Construction took about two years.

Such a large system required a lot to build—time, money and people: engineers, surveyors, draftsmen, drillers, pick and shovel laborers, mule skinners, steam and electrical equipment operators, pile drivers, concrete workers, carpenters, teamsters, foremen, nurses and doctors, cooks, clerks, timekeepers and accountants. To say nothing of the financiers who supplied the capital to keep them all working until the project began to bring in money. And they all needed someplace to live. One of the first things Filer and a survey crew did was to lay out a large construction camp.

Courtesy Twin Falls Canal Co.

Derricks suspend the cable that hold electrically operated dump carts.

The steady influx of construction workers over the duration of the project swelled the construction camp, which became the town of Milner. By early April 1903, the town boasted a temporary tent-hotel, a meat market, general store and a feedlot. The town soon added a post office, bank, hotel, livery barn, lumber yard and eventually a railroad depot. The construction company set up a temporary office building, cookhouse and toolhouse. Residents saw Milner becoming the principal town in the area. But it began to wither when the dam construction was completed. It was simply too far from the irrigated tract. Today, all that's left is a door-less concrete bank vault, which sits empty and exposed to the elements just west of the dam.

Meanwhile, workers did not find much diversion among the sagebrush. Life in camp included gambling and booze, and there were rumors of cocaine use. But most were tired after a hard ten-hour shift. In the day, tents provided the only shade. At night, a chorus of coyotes serenaded the sleeping men and the eerie scream of an occasional prowling cougar cut through the night. Pack rats made off with anything they could carry. Men were paid $1.25 to $1.50 a day for ten hours of work. They slept in tents, and ate their meals in company mess tents. Most of the men worked hard through rain or sun—in the heat of summer or the cold of winter.

Dust was their constant companion.

When the relentless Idaho west wind blew, dust from construction and the wagon roads thickened the air. The dirt was pounded to a fine volcanic grit by countless wagon wheels and horses. It rose like clouds of flour with every step. The light tan dust settled everywhere and found its way into everything—mouths and eyes, food, water, bedding and the air they breathed. When it rained, the dust turned into a sticky, slippery gumbo. It made footing difficult, yet clung to boots, making them heavy and awkward. Sun soon baked the goo brick hard.

The common perception is that the dam was built by men with shovels and horse-drawn carts dumping endless loads of rock and gravel. But that's not how it happened. It was built with modern construction methods of the day. Robert Faris and Frank Kesl's crews began by building an eight hundred foot temporary, rock-fill diversion dam below the construction site. Rock-filled cribs raised the water level about five feet and forced about one hundred cubic feet per second—or about forty-five thousand gallons per minute—of water into a channel along the canyon wall. The channel dropped the water about thirty feet to a water wheel that powered a two-hundred kilowatt, direct current generator. A water wheel in the north channel generated additional power. Together, the two generators provided the power to run the latest electrically operated construction equipment.

Cables were strung to four electric cranes on derricks—two on each side. The cranes raised large rocks to small dump-cars—each barely big enough to hold three men standing upright. The cars loaded with rock or dirt were hoisted and pulled out over the dams. When the cars reached the desired spot, a workman using an electrically operated control dumped the rock. The cars also dumped gravel and dirt for the face of the dam. Power from the generating plants ran electric drills for blasting holes in the rock, at the dam as well as the first stretch of canal. And as the canal was excavated, workers laid track to haul rock to the dam site where it was used as fill. When it came time to drill the blasting holes for the bypass tunnels beneath the south island, the workers used electric drills. The power also ran electric lights, so work could go on around the clock at times.

Courtesy Twin Falls Public Library.
A land opening on the Twin Falls Tract draws a crowd.

Construction materials came by railroad to Shoshone or the railhead at Kimama. From there, wagons hauled it to the construction site. Kimama — at twenty-seven miles from The Cedars — was closer. Most of the materials had to come across the river one way or another. Faris and Kesl brought in a steam shovel weighing 14,000 pounds. It came by rail, but it was too heavy for the suspension bridge and had to be ferried across the river.

The dam itself would consist of three separate dams in the river channels between the two islands. Each dam would be built separately, one at a time, starting with the one in the south channel. The middle section followed and was built just like the first. The north channel, the only one that carried any water all year, proved the most difficult. When finished, the dam stretched from the south bank and headed east. About two-thirds of its length across, it turned ninety degrees to head north to join the north bank. It formed roughly a right angle laid across the river, pointing generally east into the reservoir it created.

Workers began by clearing the rubble from the bottom of the south river channel and then drilling and blasting down into bedrock to form a trench twenty-nine feet deep. The trench extended into the south canyon wall and into the side of the south island and was sealed with concrete. On this, workers set a core of overlapping, two-inch-thick planks laid horizontally on edge. This thirty-five-foot high core, two planks thick, was reinforced by uprights at two foot intervals. Once the core was in place, workers carefully placed rock and dirt by hand and puddled it against the core with water. The rest was filled from the electric dump-cars that brought rock and fill to make up the face of the dam. The inner face was then covered and strengthened with riprap. The base was about 150 feet wide, with the upstream face sloping gradually, getting four feet narrower for every foot of height. The crest of the first dam from the canyon wall to the first island was 462 feet long.

At the same time, other workers started turning the south island into the main spillway. The island appeared to be solid rock and was the longer of the two. Workers began by blasting away at the tough basalt, to cut the rock down to about five feet above the level of the canal bed. After the top was cut down to the required height, a steel and concrete foundation was set in the rock to hold the casing for the ninety-nine spillway gates, which would span nearly five hundred feet. The gates were five and a half feet wide by ten feet high and were made of four-inch-thick, tongue-and-groove wooden planks. Threaded stem gears were bolted to each gate casing to raise and lower them by a mechanism mounted on a walkway above the gates.

As work progressed on the dam, company officials worked on ensuring adequate financial backing for the project. In April 1903, Frank Buhl teamed up with friend Peter Lanterman Kimberly. Kimberly was born in 1846 in Austintown, Ohio, and moved to Sharon, Pennsylvania. There he met Buhl, and the two became friends and eventually business partners. The Buhl-Kimberly Corporation was established in April in Bridgeport, Connecticut. Not until that November, however, did Kimberly visit the project in Idaho. His premature death in June 1905, before the company could be turned over to the farmers, created some temporary trouble.

The original surveys for the project burned in the fire at the company offices in Salt Lake City and had to be redone before work could start on the canals. One of the engineers Bickel had brought with him to Idaho was a young man from Missouri. John Edward Hayes had worked in Helena with Bickel on public land surveys in northwestern Montana — land that is now Glacier National Park. Filer assigned him to survey the canals.

Hayes was born November 7, 1877, in Kirkwood, Missouri. He completed high school in Carlyle, Illinois, and had been accepted at the University of Illinois as an engineering student. But the same financial panic that sank Riblett and Hansen's plans for a dam and irrigation canals at The Cedars, blocked Hayes' plans for college. During the silver panic of 1893, a bank failure wiped out the money the Hayes family had set aside. Instead, the young John Hayes set out for Colorado to work as an apprentice on mine surveys in the Cripple Creek area for his brother-in-law, Charles W. Wells, a mining engineer who had married Hayes' sister. Here he learned engineering on the job, working on patent and underground surveys. He learned the craft well enough that the state of Idaho later issued him a license.

Hayes arrived in Rock Creek in late 1902. No longer at its prime since the arrival of the railroad to the north, it remained a local gathering place for the people who were arriving in southern Idaho to work for the Twin Falls Land and Water Company on the new irrigation project. Here in this dusty crossroads, canal project workers could get a hot bath, a warm meal and a real bed for about a day's pay.

In Rock Creek, Hayes encountered a man who already had surveyed much of the terrain that Hayes now faced. John Hansen had bought the Rock Creek store in 1900 and operated it until it closed in 1916. It was one base of supplies for the construction workers on the Twin Falls Canal system. The two got to talking, and soon the talk turned to surveying and irrigation. Hansen brought out his earlier work to share with the young engineer. He showed Hayes the maps he had made with Frank Riblett. And he showed Hayes his layout for the High Line Canal. In the process, Hayes met Hansen's daughter, Anna. The two hit it off. But more about them later. For now, Hayes's most pressing job was to run the survey crews laying out what would become the High Line Canal, closely following the route Hansen had set out ten years earlier. Hayes had his hands full staying ahead of the canal construction.

The canal alignment had to be carefully calculated. His job was to find the line that kept the canal as high as possible while sustaining sufficient flow. The grade had to be steep enough to move the water along. Fast enough to keep moving, but not so fast it would erode the banks, and not so slow the silt would settle out. The grade Hayes set out dropped about nine and a half inches, per mile. Work progressed as often with a shovel and a bucket of water as a transit. Where possible, the survey crew would pour a little water on the ground and see which way it ran—with a little help from the shovel. Crews slept and ate in camps along the route they were laying out. When the line moved too far along, they collapsed the tents and loaded everything into wagons and hauled them to the next convenient campsite along the sinuous path dictated by the exacting specification of the canal grade.

While work progressed on the dam, workers following the line Hayes had laid out took two years to build the sixty-five miles of the High Line Canal. Local workers signed contracts for removing rock and dirt from canals. Where possible, canals and laterals were excavated by graders and scrapers to smooth natural obstructions. Some sections had to be cleared with pick and shovel. In some places, coulees and natural channels were pressed into service as part of the system. The finished canals varied from 80 to 120 feet wide at the bottom. The banks were two feet thick for every foot high—about twelve feet high. The top of each canal bank was wide enough for a one-lane road, which provided access for maintenance and repairs.

The electric railway was extended from the dam site into the main canal as excavation progressed. Electric drills and shovels shattered and loosened the rock. A derrick loaded the largest pieces into small open cars on narrow-gauge rails, and they were hauled to the dam site as fill. The electric railways, electric drills and a motorized grader moved a lot of dirt and rock. But the work still had to be finished by men with picks and shovels. In the areas where there was little rock, dirt was moved by about four hundred teams of horses and five hundred drivers pulling large cast iron scoops to dig canals.

Courtesy Twin Falls Public Library.
A electric rock machine moves rocks in a canal in 1903.

As the canals progressed, structures were added to control the flow of water from the dam. At the head of the main canal, Faris and Kesl built nine head gates, set in concrete on solid rock. The radial gates were twelve feet wide, with a curved height of eleven feet. Hand cranks raised and lowered the main canal gates. From the canal head gates, the main canal followed the contours of the land for nine miles to Dry Creek Reservoir, later named Murtaugh Lake for assistant canal company manager Mark Murtaugh. The reservoir was formed by a mile-long rolled-earth dam, forty-eight feet high at its highest across the low area on Dry Creek. The lake gave the canal system flexibility to regulate canal flow, providing a buffer between canal system operations and river flows. It also provided a second safety valve should the main canal gates fail. It would keep the full force of the river from overrunning the canals and the farmlands to the west. Murtaugh Lake held about eight thousand acre-feet—enough for about two days worth of irrigation.

From the lake's outlet gates set in concrete piers, the canal swings back toward the canyon around the low rise of Hansen Butte. About seven miles from the lake, the canal nears the Snake River Canyon at a spot named Point Spill for an emergency spillway installed there. Opening the two radial gates in an emergency would create one big waterfall back into the canyon. The gates could dump most of the thirty-six hundred cubic feet per second typically in the canal. It provides the most immediate relief in case of a problem.

Seven miles farther on, the main canal splits at a place dubbed The Forks. The High Line Canal continues south, and the Low Line Canal drops off to the west. The original surveys had called for a single canal about sixty-five 65 miles long, with laterals running north toward the Snake River. Hayes' survey in 1903, however, showed a more complex system would be needed to adequately irrigate the tract. He convinced officials that a second canal was needed to irrigate the entire tract efficiently.

From The Forks, the High Line meanders south for about six miles until it crosses Rock Creek. A wooden culvert was built for the creek, but it wasn't big enough. It was later replaced with gates in both canal embankments. One let the creek flow into the canal, and the other let it back out on the other side. Here, the High Line Canal turns west and follows a course similar to the Low Line Canal a couple of miles down grade. A few miles west of Rock Creek, McMillan Creek crosses the canal in a wooden culvert. And beyond that, the canal crosses Cottonwood Creek in a timber flume, four hundred feet long and supported by pillars set in concrete. Fifteen miles west, Cedar Draw joins the High Line, only to escape again through a gate on the other side, letting the natural flow continue on its way. The canal gradually shrinks as it winds its way west and laterals tap the main line. Only a small stream tumbles into Salmon Falls Creek at the west end of the project, forty-seven miles from The Forks.

At The Forks, the Low Line Canal drops eighty feet over a half mile. To slow erosion, the channel was strengthened with riprap. The drop was intended at some time to be put to work in a hydroelectric plant, which was eventually built in the 1980s. About three miles down, the Low Line intersects Perrine Coulee, where a check dam spills water into the coulee, putting it to work as part of the system. The coulee splits into two laterals through the city of Twin Falls. About three miles beyond Perrine Coulee, Rock Creek Canyon stopped the Low Line. The canyon is about eighty feet deep at this point. Completion had to wait for the construction of a means to get water across the canyon. Meanwhile, work on the Low Line continued west on the other side of the canyon. Beyond Rock Creek, the Low Line Canal crosses Cedar Draw in a wooden walled flume, similar to the flume that carried the High Line over Cottonwood Creek. The Low Line runs into Deep Creek, and the water is distributed in smaller laterals. But no water would run until the crossing over Rock Creek was completed.

Toward the end of June 1903, workers started blasting their way through the base of the south island for eight bypass tunnels that would divert the flow of the river while they built the dam in the north channel. About the same time, company officials were getting ready for the first drawing for land on the Twin Falls tract, offering an opening of sixty thousand acres. The company borrowed $40,000 for advertising the land opening across the country. They sent out thousands of single-page tracts describing the land and the opening. Ads ran in the *New York Times* in March and later in the *Portland Oregonian*, the *Salt Lake Herald* and the *Idaho Statesman* in Boise. Ads also ran in the *Albion Times* and the *Shoshone Journal*. The ads included directions to the drawing in Shoshone, which had a railroad station and banks.

The date was set for July 1, 1903.

The company advertised land for fifty cents per acre and the water rights for twenty-five dollars per acre, with a down payment of twenty-five cents per acre for the land and three dollars per acre for the water and ten years to pay off the rest. Anyone who wanted to be included in the drawing had to apply in person or through an agent. Individuals put their names in a box. When a name was picked, that person could pick out up to a quarter section—160—pay a deposit, and sign a ten-year contract with the Twin Falls Land and Water Company for the balance. The typical quarter section would have required a deposit of $520 — $40 for the land and $480 for the water. The remaining $3,560 was due within ten years. The total paid for the 160 acres and the water to irrigate it would add up to $4,080. The Carey Act gave the would-be farmer three years to start irrigating and farming a portion of the land. The land was then his when he paid the other twenty-five cents per acre.

Walter Filer, Paul Bickel and Frank Buhl were on hand for the drawing in Shoshone. They anticipated long lines. But the anticipated thousands failed to show up. Several hundred people came, but only fifty-seven names were dropped into the box for the drawing, and only thirty actually filed. It was a disaster. Some thought the opening was simply too early. At the time, the company was asking people to invest in surveyed sageland and a promise of water that was still two years off. It was too little for most. People who visited the project were awed by its scope and the impossible task of harnessing the raging north channel. Leveling the tops of two basalt islands, blasting tunnels capable of taking the whole river through the bottom of the bigger island — the whole thing seemed impossible. Pessimists refused to believe it could be done. Too many believed the skeptics who maintained that if a dam could even be built across the river, it would never hold water; and if it did, the canals would wash out or the land would turn alkali.

Among those who filed were some of Perrine's family members, and Jacob Fertz, Stanley Milner and Burt Perrine's friend Robert McCollum. The first name drawn was hydro developer Harry Hollister, who got one hundred sixty acres a mile south of Shoshone Falls.

Buhl, who had come to Idaho for the land opening, went home disappointed and discouraged. He called Filer and Perrine to Chicago for a meeting. Buhl blamed Perrine for overselling the project that Buhl now thought was doomed to failure. He had let himself be persuaded by Perrine, who knew nothing about business. But Perrine remained convinced by his own twenty years in the canyon. He denied having tried to trick Buhl and insisted the project needed only the right kind of promotion. Indomitable, Perrine convinced Buhl that the project wasn't hopeless. He insisted he could make it work, and claimed he could prove it if Buhl would give him five years. Swayed by Perrine's enthusiasm and conviction, Buhl gave in again. But he demanded a guarantee. The two drew up a contract in which Perrine agreed to sell twenty-five thousand acres per year for five years as well as lots in a town that still was a sagebrush desert. Both signed the contract.

Perrine knew he needed to show the farmers more than just a promise of water. He was determined. Buhl was resigned.

Courtesy Twin Falls Canal Co.
Construction detail shows the wood plank core of Milner Dam.

Chapter Eight:
Building the Town

One sunny day in mid-September 1903, in the unbroken sagebrush sea, John Hayes set a small white flag, marking a corner of a square-mile section of land. The section would become a city at the epicenter of the largest Carey Act irrigation project in the country. Hayes thought it an excellent site. The well-drained land sloped gently toward the scenic Rock Creek Canyon. He envisioned a lake with people boating and fishing, with acres of tree-shaded parkways. But because the name Shoshone already had been taken for another town, the project engineers had agreed to name the new city after the second largest waterfall in the area — they called it Twin Falls.

This section — Section 16 of Township 10 South, Range 17 East, Boise Meridian — was picked because it was a school section (state land already set aside and available as a town site). A school section could be acquired without proving up, and this one was about in the center of the project. The site was a few miles south of Burt Perrine's Blue Lakes Ranch and only six miles from the storied Shoshone Falls, "Niagara of the West." And selecting, surveying and selling lots in a town site was part of the deal Burt Perrine had made with Frank Buhl to keep the project alive. Despite his misgivings after the dismal showing for the land opening in July, Buhl upheld his end of the deal, and the project went forward. Both faced challenges ahead. Technical difficulties with the dam construction and crossing Rock Creek challenged Buhl's engineers and threatened to undermine confidence in the project. Perrine had to show enough progress to attract farmers to invest. The test of his efforts was less than a year off, in the second land opening set for October 1904. Perrine put his enthusiasm to work promoting the project.

Work progressed on the dam and the canals over the winter.

Then in April 1904, Hayes set out again to complete the survey of the town site he had flagged back in September. Starting from that white flag, he established corners and set a marker at what would be the main intersection of downtown Twin Falls. Hayes staked out four city blocks at the center of a town of sagebrush, its only human inhabitants were the survey crew members. He filed his plat with the county in Albion on May 12, 1904. On June 1, Frank Buhl, Stanley Milner and Martin B. DeLong formed the Twin Falls Townsite Company and incorporated in Utah. With stock worth $150,000, the principal stockholder was Buhl. The other stockholders had only one share each. Lots were selected for a bank, hotel and a store, and fourteen blocks were added to the earlier plat.

John Hayes

The town site company hired French architect Emmanuel Louis Masquerey to plan the city. The most notable feature was the 45-degree layout of the streets instead of the more standard north-south alignment, in a region where most roads followed the rigidly rectangular surveyed section lines. Not all local residents agree on the reasons for the catty-cornered layout. Some say it was so sun would shine on all four sides of the houses in town. Some say it was so folks wouldn't have the sun in their eyes while driving a wagon through town. Others say it was so the relentless west wind wouldn't howl unimpeded down city streets.

Hayes and his crews worked through the summer. By late September 1904 all available lots had been sold, even before Hayes had filed the final plat on October 4, 1904. Construction in town began at once. The first school was built before the first saloon. The first city land was sold to an engineer on the Oregon Short Line, George Walters, on August 1, 1904. Homes, businesses and churches began to go up. Perrine's friend and erstwhile partner, Robert McCollum, the Shoshone publisher who had backed out of his $1 share in the filing fees for the water right at The Cedars, built the first house in the new town of Twin Falls, at 708 East Shoshone Street. People were betting the project would succeed, for without the water, all the dreams manifest in brick, clapboard and shingles would collapse.

The only other towns in the region at the time were Shoshone, Rock Creek and the county seat, Albion. Everything had to be hauled by wagon from the railroad station in Shoshone, the railhead at Kimama, or by wagon from Kelton, until the railroad arrived in Twin Falls in the summer of 1905. From Shoshone, the road was thirty-five miles through sagebrush, and down into the Snake River Canyon. The choices were hazardous. At Shoshone Falls, an open ferry crossed the whirling waters. A few miles downstream, a steep, rocky grade and hairpin turns led down to Perrine's Blue Lakes Ranch, crossed on a wooden bridge, wound behind a waterfall and clambered up the other side. What is now the main north-south street through town, Blue Lakes Boulevard, then was but a cleared path through the sagebrush from Shoshone via Perrine's Blue Lakes ranch. The dust sometimes was a foot deep; when it rained the mud seemed deeper.

The city was officially incorporated April 13, 1905.

While Hayes and his survey crews mapped the new town, Walter Filer kept his crews busy on the three dam sections that would join the two islands in the river. The dam in the middle channel went up following the same process as the first dam. Workers cleared the river bottom of rubble, cut a trench and filled it with concrete. They set a wooden plank core in place and added rock and dirt fill. When they were done, the middle dam spanned 404 feet. While that was going on, other crews started drilling, blasting and grading the top of the north island for a second, 290-foot-long spillway. It would serve during high flows or during repairs to the main spillway. A concrete weir topped with gates allowed water to flow over the island during high water.

Meanwhile, tunnelers had gone to work beneath the south island. The tunnels would divert the river while the dam in the north channel was built, and they had to be completed before work on the dam could start. First workers made a deep cut in the upstream side of the island, level with and curving in from the river's north channel to the tunnels. They built a fifteen-foot-high concrete wall along the cut. A temporary cofferdam would keep the river away until the tunnels were completed. Despite this effort, water leaked into the open cut between the north channel and the tunnels.

Courtesy Twin Falls Canal Co.

Workers blasted and dug tunnels beneath the second island to divert the flow of the Snake River during construction of the third dam section.

Then, men with electric drills went to work on the upstream face of the island. Others started drilling and blasting on a similar cut on the downstream side below riverbed level. Like the Chinese crews that blasted their way through the Sierra Nevada for the Central Pacific Railroad forty years earlier, crews blasted eight tunnels horizontally through the seemingly solid rock at the bottom of the cut. Like miners, they shored the tunnel ceilings with columns and I-beams as they progressed. But then they hit an unexpected, wide seam of clay in what everyone had thought was solid rock. They made the concrete side walls thicker to ensure the seam was properly sealed so water would not erode the clay, undermining the entire island. Center columns and tunnel dividers also were encased in concrete. But concrete and wood to line the tunnels were expensive. Lumber had to be brought in on wagons. Gravel for the concrete was made in two electric rock crushers on site. When completed, the tunnels were four feet wide, eight feet high and varied in length from 80 to 120 feet. Metal gates were installed on the upstream face to close the tunnels when their job was done. Wheels would turn the long screw-shafts operated from the top of the island when the time came.

In June 1904, work crews blew up the cofferdams that had kept the river from the bypass tunnels. Filer was satisfied that the tunnels would hold up to the full flow of the river, and he gave the order. Moments later the river began flowing down the cut, into the tunnels and under the south island. With the river diverted, work could begin on the third dam section.

In August, the derricks that suspended the electric gondolas were moved and work began on the north dam. From the second island, the dam would run north. But here Filer ran into trouble. The north channel was lower than the other two and some water still flowed here, despite the bypass tunnels. The job would take longer than planned, and it would require crews of drillers, teams of divers and railcar loads of Portland cement. Workers using the gondolas slung from the cables, dumped rocks in the river to form two cofferdams to divert more water into the cut channel and the completed tunnels. Even with the cofferdams in place and the tunnels wide open, it was impossible to cut the flow in the north channel completely.

Work on the base of the dam had to be done under water. Divers cleared rocks from the bottom of the channel and secured rock-filled wooden cribs lowered by cranes. With the cribs in place, they attached planking to the bottom with concrete lowered in sacks. On land nearby, workers assembled a wooden core in a single large piece, similar to those at the center of the two other dam sections. They lowered it into place and divers set it in concrete. The process was slow and laborious and fraught with delays. Divers took longer than expected to clear rock from the bottom of the channel. During the process, one of the towers holding the cables for the tram collapsed under a load of rock. Current washed away fill dirt.

In November 1904, the core in the north channel dam was set into place; almost immediately the water behind it began to rise.

Perrine's first attempts to find someone to finance the promotion of the Twin Falls tract fell through. Through friends at the Corn Exchange Bank of Chicago, however, Perrine secured a loan to promote the project. He formed the Perrine City Investment Company with C.B. Hurt as president, Perrine as vice president and Bob McCollum as secretary-treasurer. John Crocker, Tom Costello and B. Salmond were directors. The loan was in the form of 600,000 bonds at one dollar each, issued by Trowbridge and Niven of Chicago. The first thing they did was hire Mark Bennett of Chicago, the publicity man who had promoted the world fairs in Buffalo and St. Louis. Full page advertisements in metropolitan newspapers promoted the opportunities in southern Idaho and quoted a scientist from Washington State College on the productivity of the soil. Bennett also insisted that building a fancy hotel at the town site was essential to convince investors. Uncertain, Perrine and other investors went along. With the town site established and buildings under construction, work also began on the hotel. It certainly gave the impression of confidence. Perrine wanted to name it for Buhl's partner Peter Kimberly, but others prevailed and it became — and stayed — the Perrine Hotel.

In September 1904, John Crocker, Tom Costello and Walter Perrish chartered a Pullman car and brought twenty farmers from Illinois to Idaho to show them established irrigated farms and then to the Twin Falls tract to see the land and the progress on the project. All but one filed for land the following month. Other excursions followed. By this time, two sections of the dam were completed and work was progressing on the third. The canals were snaking their way across the landscape. And in the middle of the tract, a town was taking shape, with buildings going up, including the hotel. Tests had shown the soil was excellent. Farmers need only clear the sagebrush and apply irrigation water. Test crops of grains, vegetables, sugar beets, grasses and melons showed good results. All that was needed was irrigation water. And that was coming, Perrine promised.

By the second land opening in October 1904, the project promoters could show plenty of promise—considerably more than potential buyers had seen at the previous summer's disastrous initial land opening. Their work paid off, and Bennett's instincts were good. The second opening exceeded even Perrine's optimistic expectations. With the first year up on the contract, Perrine reported to Buhl that the company had sold 117,000 acres—only 8,000 acres short of what he had promised to do within five years.

But important work remained to be done on the canals. The Low Line Canal followed the contours of the land until it reached the deepening canyon of Rock Creek about four miles south of the present-day town of Kimberly. Near the bottom, the sides sloped with accumulated talus, and the creek ran in a narrow channel perhaps twenty feet wide. It was lined with willows and strewn with basketball-sized basalt boulders. Though the canals were completed on both sides, no water would flow down the Low Line until engineers found a way to carry the canal across the canyon.

As most any grade-school science student knows, water seeks its own level. Engineers settled on an inverted siphon, a principle that Roman engineers used on that ancient city's aqueducts. The steel pipe for the siphon at Rock Creek was built in Sharon, Pennsylvania, at Frank Buhl's Sharon Boiler Works. The five-foot-wide, half-circle sections began arriving at the railhead at Kimama in January 1905. From there they were loaded onto wagons and hauled to the site where they would be assembled. Sharon Boiler Works sent a crew along to install the pipe, with pneumatic drills and riveters. The crew laid the sections in a trench and wooden framework as they riveted the pieces together. They added steel reinforcing bands halfway between the section seams. Crews drilled out the rock of the canyon walls to form a base for the steel tube. The inlet and outlet were set in concrete structures. A manhole entry opened at the top of the pipe and a six-inch drain tapped its lowest point.

Courtesy Twin Falls Canal Co.

The Siphon nears completion in early 1905.

When completed, the ten-foot diameter steel pipe dropped eighty feet to the bottom of the canyon. It crossed the creek, turned up again, and 440 feet from the inlet, water gushed forth on the other side of the canyon. This inverted siphon—known simply as The Siphon—formed the key link to a substantial portion of the canal system.

As February 1905 drew to a close, work crews completed the dam and closed the tunnel gates. It had taken the engineers and construction crews six months to complete the 280-foot north dam.

It was the shortest of the three dams, but the most difficult. They had started August 1904 and finished at the end of January 1905. Satisfied with the progress, company officials set March 1 as the official opening of the canal system. The bypass tunnels in Milner Dam would be closed to fill the reservoir. The following morning the canal head gates would be opened to start water flowing in the canals. It would be a momentous day, the moment of truth for everyone involved with the system and its construction. This would be the day backers and supporters of this grand idea hoped to prove the fears of skeptics unfounded.

Officials, workers and onlookers, keyed with expectation, gathered on top of Milner Dam to turn the cranks that would wind down the bypass gates, closing the tunnels and shutting off the flow beneath the island. As the gates closed the flow diminished and nearly stopped. But not completely. One of the gates would not close, and water continued to flow through the tunnel. Divers sent down to investigate found a rail lodged in one of the gates. Buhl and Kimberly had telegraphed that they would be late for the opening, but urged company officials not to wait for them. When they arrived, however, divers still were working on the tunnel gates. They pulled the rail out, and when the gate was closed they sealed it with sandbags. The reservoir level began to rise again.

That night Shoshone Falls went dry. Rumor has it that hundreds of gold seekers headed out onto bare rocks above the falls to pick up an expected bonanza of gold normally covered with rushing waters. Most would have been disappointed. But even as Shoshone Falls went dry, it began to appear that the skeptics might be right. The night brought disappointment instead of jubilation. Dirt fill in the north dam caved in, and it began to leak. The tunnel gates were raised, taking the full flow of the Snake River. The reservoir level dropped again even as people began to gather for the opening of the canal head gates.

Plans for the opening looked uncertain.

Chapter Nine:
Water on the Land

A dry, scratchy whisper grew to a soft gurgle, as a thin sheet of muddy water pushed tumbleweeds along the dry canal bottom of the head-gate structure. Water began flowing into the canal on the morning of March 2, 1905. About two thousand onlookers had gathered, and Walter Filer turned the wheel of the winch that cranked the first gate open at the head of the canal. Mark Murtaugh's wife, Elizabeth, poured a bottle of champagne into the water as it entered the canal. The onlookers cheered.

Nothing would ever be the same in south-central Idaho. This was the moment farmers and company backers had long been waiting for. Water arrived as promised, and in time for the land's first irrigation season. But it was a tenuous start, as the leaking dam drained some of the enthusiasm from the opening festivities. Even as water began flowing into the canal, the reservoir level was dropping. The tunnel gates had been cranked open to allow repairs on the leaking north dam section.

On March 3, the reservoir level had dropped enough to allow work to proceed. With the ceremonial opening over, Filer and Murtaugh got busy trying to plug the leak. They directed a long line of wagons loaded with dirt, cinders, crushed rock and gravel as crews sluiced it into the upstream face of the north dam section. But new material continued to cave in. Workers drove in sheet piling to stem the stubborn leak. Efforts continued, but not until March 13 could Murtaugh report that the leak was finally stopped. Divers again went down to reseal the tunnel gates. The dam was finally holding back the river. Most of the water now flowed into the canal on the south side, and some went over the spillway, uprooting the last of the trees that had given the place its name. The north dam continued to cause problems, however, and required additional work in the following years before the system could be turned over to irrigators. But more water flowed through the canal gates, and the level in the canals was allowed to rise only a little at a time to let the embankments strengthen as they slowly soaked up water. It took about two months before water filled the still incomplete canal system.

Courtesy of Twin Falls Canal Co.

Elizabeth Murtaugh holds a bottle of champagne during the opening ceremony as her husband, Mark Murtaugh, and Frank Buhl, Peter Kimberly, Walter Filer and others crank open the Twin Falls Canal head gates March 2, 2005. Hundreds of onlookers gathered on the bank out of sight.

The canals created streams where before had been only dry grasses and a forest of sagebrush. By summer, a patchwork of green was beginning to show on the south side. The first year 15,000 acres were under irrigation, and by the second year, that grew to 130,000 acres. The patchwork of farms eventually would cover more than three hundred square miles. But there was much to be done before the system could begin providing irrigation water to the entire tract. And in a larger sense, the work would never be done.

Until The Siphon was completed, water in the Low Line was diverted down the Perrine Coulee through Twin Falls. Then on May 14, Murtaugh reported that The Siphon was complete and moving water across Rock Creek. During the height of the irrigation season, it would carry more than eleven hundred cubic feet of water per second—that's about half a million gallons per minute. It would bring irrigation water to eighty thousand acres, or about 40 percent of the Twin Falls tract.

George A. Lincoln moved from a Mormon family home in Utah to southeastern Idaho in the late 1800s. He settled with his wife and family in Grays Lake where he ran a general store. But the panic of 1893 undermined the economy and eventually his business. He struggled for a while. When he heard of the Twin Falls project he brought his two sons, expecting to find work. Lincoln signed on with a survey crew, laying out and building the High Line Canal. Home was a tent in a Rock Creek construction camp. Meanwhile, his wife soon tired of waiting for him to return, so she packed up the bedding and the dishes, loaded them on a wagon and followed after him. When Lincoln looked up one day and saw the wagon come over the hill, he knew he was here for good. That was two years before the water would start flowing. He filed on a piece of land south of the present town of Filer. His son bought a place nearby in 1914. And for many years his grandson, Wayne Lincoln, served as a canal company board member and still farms the spread his father bought.

Like Lincoln, farmers began arriving on the tract long before the water did. A few came with the first land opening in the summer of 1903. Others came looking for work and ended up putting their earnings into a share of the system. Work was easy to find in southern Idaho in those days. Many men cleared sagebrush or joined one of the construction crews on the canal system to earn a living until the water made raising and selling a crop possible. Most arrived with youth and enthusiasm. Before the land could be farmed, however, it had to be cleared and leveled. The ditches had to be dug and homes built. Settlers set up tents and started to clear sagebrush, dig ditches and wells, build houses and sheds and get ready for winter. Many lived in simple shacks, the first year or two. They had to contend with wind, dust and not a tree in sight. Until the canal water arrived, they could buy water for ten cents a bucketful. But it was so muddy, it had to sit for a while to settle, and then it had to be boiled before it could be used.

The land was covered with tough sagebrush two to six feet tall. Clearing sagebrush, however, was cheaper and easier than clearing trees from even lightly timbered lands in the East. At first people cleared it by hand, chopping or grubbing out the stubborn, deep-rooted brush. Later, they started using horses. A man and a team of four horses could clear about an acre per day. The most common way was to hitch the horses to an iron rail or heavy-toothed rake to break down the sagebrush. One man could clear eighty acres in a single summer. The uprooted sagebrush was gathered into piles and burned. Some people scavenged the big pieces for firewood. Many fires burned after dark, dotting the nighttime plains with bright flickering lights.

But the work wasn't over. Once the sagebrush was gone, farmers still had to level the land so water would flow evenly across the fields without washing out crops. Without leveling, some parts of the field would be too wet and others too dry. Most farmers used a horse-drawn scraper to move dirt from high spots to the low spots. Irrigation water arrived at the farmers' head gates in canal company ditches. Typically, farmers dug smaller ditches to bring irrigation water to the upper end of the fields. They turned water onto fields by making openings in the ditch banks with a small-bladed shovel to flood the fields. That early method has since been replaced with siphon tubes, gated pipe and sprinklers. The siphon tube is a curved piece of aluminum tubing about two feet long and three-quarters of an inch in diameter— some are larger. A farmer pushes the pipe into the ditch water, plugs the open end with a thumb and pulls it back. Repeating the motion rapidly several times fills the tube with water. An experienced hand makes it look easy. Then the tube is laid with one end still in the ditch and the other end in one of the small furrows, known as "corrugates." Voila'. A little stream of water trickles from the siphon down the corrugate.

Once adequately watered, the virgin lava soil produced bountiful crops. Farmers grew rye, barley, millet, clover and winter wheat. They added potatoes, corn, beans and fruit orchards. Wheat grew well and required less water, especially late in the season. Farmers often resorted to growing wheat in dry years. Tests in 1906 showed one acre would grow eighty-four bushels of wheat, one hundred nineteen bushels of oats, twenty-one tons of beets or six tons of alfalfa.

Almost one-third of the land grew alfalfa. It was a versatile crop, adapted to local soil conditions, and sold as hay or to produce seed. Farmers could get three or four cuttings in most years. Alfalfa also helped build up the soil. Most was sold locally as livestock feed. Desperate ranchers bought all the hay they could get for winter. Overgrazing in the 1880s had depleted the native grasses on southern Idaho rangelands and left too little forage for cattle to survive bad winters.

Idaho's reputation for growing potatoes goes back to 1890, when farmers started growing them for mining camps. With good soil, lots of sun and irrigation water, an acre on the Twin Falls tract could yield 200 bushels of record size spuds, or 150 tons per acre.

But there was no local market for that many potatoes.

The railroad arrived in Twin Falls only five months after the water, and before the first harvest. But its origins go back to the building of the continental railroad in the 1860s. Union Pacific President Sidney Dillon took up the idea of the UP's own Pacific Connection. Starting at Granger, Wyoming, construction on UP's Oregon Short Line began in 1881, reached Shoshone in May 1883 and Huntington, Oregon, in 1884.

Before the railroad arrived, most agriculture in southern Idaho served local markets. Farmers raised hay for draft animals and livestock, and they sold wheat, fruit and vegetables to miners. The railroad opened the national market for Idaho potatoes and other crops. In 1882, Idaho was growing about 2,000 acres of potatoes. By 1900 that was up to more than 9,000 acres, and by the beginning of World War I, it was more than 30,000 acres. The Oregon Short Line reported shipping thousands of cars of potatoes out of Idaho, and encouraged farmers to grow more. Apples and potatoes from Idaho were sold in the Chicago area—Oak Park, Evanston and La Grange—through mail order by the train load.

In 1885, Union Pacific President Charles F. Adams, who had seen the potential for irrigation in southern Idaho, recommended adding branch lines. The Oregon Short Line reached Minidoka on January 13, 1883. But it would be more than twenty years before work started on a branch line to Twin Falls. When work began on Milner Dam in 1903, the railroad was still about thirty-five miles away in Shoshone or Kimama. Even in those days, that was a long trip by horse and wagon or stagecoach to bring passengers and freight to the tract. The trip included a descent into the canyon and a ferry across the river. Developers of the Twin Falls project were keenly aware of the need to attract the railroad. Project manager Walter Filer and his assistant Mark Murtaugh started out, after all, as railroad engineers. They knew that a railroad connection to the Oregon Short Line would be vital to the success of the canal system. In the West at the turn of the century a town without a railroad was doomed. Rails carried people out to settle the land, brought in supplies and hauled crops to market. They began negotiations with the railroad, even before construction started.

When questions arose about building a railroad line into Twin Falls, Twin Falls Investment Company agreed to back the gamble with 6.25 percent bonds. That helped. The Minidoka and Southwestern Railroad Company was incorporated January 18, 1904. In October, the railroad agreed to start construction by the following January on this Oregon Short Line branch, extending iron rails into what was soon to become one of the richest agricultural and commercial regions in the West. The Twin Falls Land and Water Company agreed to complete the dam and twenty-five miles of canal by June 15, 1905. Meanwhile, the railroad wanted a prelimi-

nary location and the route surveyed across the town site to estimate the distance. Railroad officials began to secure rights of way.
But they ran into some difficulty. Some farmers were reluctant to
sign right-of-way releases because they feared they were paying
for water and land that would be taken up by the railroad.
Late December in1904, the rights were secured, and construction on the roadbed got started in early January 1905 as promised.
Once the track laying started, the work progressed rapidly. Work
on the roadbed reached Milner when the dam gates were closed
on March 1. By mid-June, the tracks were a mile past the dam. On
July 21, officials projected the first train would arrive in Twin Falls
on August 7. Track was spiked into Twin Falls on July 28—the day
after the telegraph wire was strung—fifty-nine miles from Minidoka.

True to earlier prediction, the first train arrived just past noon
on a hot, dusty August 7, 1905. Engine No. 619 chugged into Twin
Falls, pulling five stuffy coaches crowded with 175 passengers. It
wheezed to a stop in front of a crowd of well-wishers. The arrival
of that train was symbolic of future prosperity. The importance of
the railroad did not escape local residents, who set aside August 7
as Railroad Day. An estimated five thousand people joined the
celebration, and two cows and six sheep were barbecued outside
the still unfinished Perrine Hotel. Speakers praised the Carey Act
and the vision of Burt Perrine.

After the festivities, the railroad crews, finished with the track,
went to work building a station and a four-stall engine house to
service steam locomotives in Twin Falls. The train eliminated the
long, arduous wagon ride from Shoshone, making it easier to get
goods and people into town. To help with the settlement, the railroad offered special immigrant cars to bring farmers, their families, livestock, machinery and household goods. The first shipment
of local livestock out of Twin Falls was five thousand sheep,
loaded in September 1905. Rail cars soon were hauling beans,
beets, potatoes and fruit. In 1912, the railroad hauled twenty-five
thousand car loads of produce from Twin Falls farms.

It was a good investment that paid for itself. The railroad company never called the bond. During 1906 and 1907, the line ran
about fifteen miles to Buhl, and eventually it was extended to the
south. The first twenty-nine miles were laid to Rogerson in 1909-

10 by the Minidoka and Southwestern. The rest was built in 1924-25 and reached 123 miles to Wells, Nevada, in 1926, where it connected with the Central Pacific Railroad.

Despite its rawboned, dusty nature, Twin Falls was considered a modern town, because it had electricity generated at Harry Hollister's Shoshone Falls power plant. John and Anna Hayes lived at 701 Shoshone Street. It was an exciting time, said Hayes's daughter, Winifred Hayes Baldwin, from her home in Virginia many years later, recalling stories from her mother. Young men made the desert bloom, built canals with horses and scrapers. Her father had been in the thick of it. "Working to him was more fun than anything else," she said. He never took a vacation.

Hayes worked as chief surveyor for the canal company from 1902 to 1909. He loved automobiles and was the first person in Twin Falls to own a car. He also was the first to live in an all-electric home. Hayes had a passion about books, she said. He would order wooden crates of books about everything. They left Twin Falls when Winifred was about three and moved to Denver, where she lived most of her life.

But Hayes returned to Twin Falls to play key roles in the canal company project and the development of the city. In 1929, he went to work as chief engineer and manager of the Twin Falls Canal Company. He also worked as engineer for the city. He protested the destruction of trees and formed the Rotary Committee to Save the Trees in what now is City Park in downtown Twin Falls. Today a variety of mature trees fill the park. Hayes also earned his reputation as a perfectionist. When trying to set up a large Christmas tree in the center of town workmen accidentally dug up the original town survey marker at the corner of Shoshone Street and Main Avenue, from which everything in the city was measured. He wouldn't rest until, with his notes and a star shot, he was able to replace the marker exactly.

Hayes had picked the town site for the scenic view out over park-like Rock Creek Canyon. But in later years the town turned its back on the canyon, dumping raw sewage into the creek until the city built a treatment plant in the 1960s. Only in recent years have some local residents begun a serious effort to clean up the creek.

While Hayes' survey crews had been busy with transits and stakes, his long-time friend, Burt Perrine, had been busy promoting the project and raising prize-winning fruit. He had taken some of his fruit to the World Exposition in Paris in 1891, where he won a first prize. He won prizes for his apples in 1900 and prizes at Buffalo, New York, in 1901, Omaha in 1902, St. Louis in 1904, Portland in 1905 and a gold medal for prunes in Seattle in 1909.

Perrine lived long enough to see the dam and canal system paid off and free of debt in March 1929. He died on October 2, 1934, at 82. John E. Hayes was a pallbearer at his funeral. Hayes died in April 1962, shortly after being re-elected as county surveyor.

For Twin Falls, 1905 was a watershed year. The Milner Dam gates closed March 1, and the canal gates opened March 2, spreading water out through the still unfinished canal system. The city of Twin Falls was incorporated April 13, and its first mayor was chief engineer Paul Bickel—an elementary school named for him still stands. The telegraph line arrived July 27 and railroad tracks the following day. The first train chugged into town on August 7. On Christmas Day 1905, a spanking new hotel named for Burt Perrine opened. The hotel, designed by J. Flood Walker, had running water from Rock Creek, uniformed bellboys, and electricity (from a generator run by a threshing machine engine) that lit the crystal chandeliers. Materials had come by wagon from Shoshone and across the river. It boasted fifty rooms, and among the first guests were John and Anna Hayes. The proud and hopeful structure lasted more than sixty years. Over that time, the guest list included Gary Cooper and Bing Crosby. It was torn down in 1968.

When it opened, the Perrine Hotel stood nearly alone in the desert, electric lights blazing, in a place where just a few years earlier only the moon and stars had broken the night, and only the howl of coyotes had carried on the wind.

Two years later, in 1907, the canal system was completed, and the planning began for turning it over to the farmers. Early in

1907, the canal system structures were assessed, including the dam and the major structures along the canals. The tunnels, canal piers, spills and checks had to be inspected and any problems noted. The deficiencies had to be fixed before the system could be turned over to the farmers. By December, they began to get impatient with the progress and filed suit to force the Twin Falls Land and Water Company to complete the system. The company finished most of the work and fixed most of the problems, but trouble continued to plague the dam. Repairs would take nearly two more years.

Twin Falls was growing and other towns on the tract began to spring up—Buhl, Kimberly, Hansen, Murtaugh. Local papers called the project a triumph of capitalism; private wealth was risked to make it possible. The final tally for the Twin Falls tract showed the canal system cost about $3.5 million. In 1909, the gross income on the tract was about $5.05 million.

On September 15, 1909, farmers agreed to accept the system despite another serious leak in Milner Dam just a few days earlier. Ten days later, on September 25, they formed the Twin Falls Canal Company. It would own, maintain and operate the system and distribute water. But it could not take ownership until repairs to the dam were completed. Finally, on October 1, the state engineer inspected and approved the system. The Twin Falls Land and Water Company turned over operations to the Twin Falls Canal Company on October 25, 1909. The canal company took over management and operation of the canal system from a brand new, handsome red brick building on the corner of Second Avenue West and Second Street West in downtown Twin Falls. The building still stands, nominated for inclusion in the National Historic Register.

But no sooner was the water flowing, than the water fights started.

In 1908, the Twin Falls Land and Water Company filed a complaint that upstream diversions were depriving the company of its full water right. The state claimed it had no authority to interfere with water distribution until the priorities had been decreed or licensed. In 1913, after it was formally established, the Twin Falls Canal Company filed a complaint against Charles Foster and other parties—including the North Side Canal Company and the federal government as operator of the Minidoka Dam, which was completed in 1909. The case went to court on June 13, 1913. One week later, the so-called Foster Decree was issued. The decree was essentially an agreement among the lower valley water users that established rights, priorities and diversion points. The decree recognized the canal company's October 11, 1900, priority.

Some of the fights came from within the Twin Falls tract. In 1910, when the canal company refused to provide water to his land, H.G. West asked the state Land Board to force the canal company to provide the water. The canal company argued that there was not enough water to supply all the acres in the Land and Water Company's contract with the state. The system was too small and the evaporation and seepage losses too high. The canal company's appropriation of three thousand cubic feet per second would have been enough, in theory, to supply 240,000 acres. But 30 percent losses to evaporation and seepage left only 2,100 cubic feet of flow–enough to irrigate only 168,000 acres. The company already had sold 195,000 acres. West's complaint asked the canal company to halt land sales.

The state Supreme Court ordered the canal company to deliver the water. The Court held that the water appropriation granted by the state engineer was technically enough for 240,000 acres. The appropriation was to be measured at the point of diversion, not somewhere else along the canal system. If the canal company had to impose some kind of rotational system to ensure everybody got water, that was something it would have to arrange. Earlier assessments had reported the system was inadequate for the amount of water it was to deliver. The canal company in turn sued the Land and Water Company to recover damages for not completing the canal system in accordance with the state contract. That suit went to court in September 1912. The canal company won the hard fought lawsuit, and the Land and Water Company paid $33,000 in damages.

Later improvements in efficiency enabled the canal company to supply water to 202,000 acres, which it still does today. The earlier estimates simply had not taken into account the seepage and evaporation.

Despite the 1913 Foster Decree, a disagreement arose in 1915 between the North Side and Twin Falls canal companies over who should get how much water. U.S. District Court Judge Frank S. Dietrich in Boise tried to settle the dispute. In June 1915, he outlined a basis for adjudicating the water rights. And in December he ruled on distribution, operation and maintenance of North and South side water rights at Milner Dam, setting up the system of shared responsibility that exists today.

The Twin Falls Canal Company diverts about 3,600 cubic feet per second at Milner, more than enough to supply all 202,000 acres with one cubic foot per eighty acres and a little left over for leaks, seepage and evaporation. The average water loss is about 15 percent. At one share per acre, each share is officially entitled to five-eighths of a miner's inch of water. A miner's inch originally was the inexact measure of flow through a hole in a sheet of metal set in a ditch or head gate. In Idaho, the miner's inch is the flow through a one-inch square hole under four inches of water, according to a University of Idaho handbook for ditch riders and water users published in 1922. That is one-fiftieth of a cubic foot per second.

Meanwhile, in 1909, the company set its annual shareholders meeting on the second Tuesday in January, during which a five-member board would be elected, and policies formulated. The board would meet twice a month. The costs to operate and maintain the system at the outset were fifty cents per share. The company later raised that to $3. It stayed low for decades, but in recent years increasing and long overdue maintenance needs drove up the cost. In 2001 shares jumped to $18 each. They have since gone to $24. Daily operations are overseen by a general manager, who today manages more than eighty full-time employees, including three water masters and twenty-seven ditch riders. Together they keep an eye on 120 miles of main canals and more than 1,000 miles of laterals and coulees. Each ditch rider covers about seventy-five hundred acres with one hundred head gates to tend in accordance with the farmers' shares. The longest "ride" is eighty-five miles. They also keep a sharp eye out for hazards, rodents, badgers and leaks.

Chapter Ten:
Working the Land

Like his father before him, Brian Olmstead knows the value of his topsoil, and he wants to keep it on his fields. He farms about seven hundred acres south of Twin Falls, including the farm established by his grandfather. He recognizes the effects irrigated agriculture can have on the land and the Snake River that is the source of the water. For twenty years, he has been trying to reduce erosion from his fields, and more importantly to keep the topsoil where it belongs. But most other farmers who irrigate with the water diverted at Milner Dam only recently began paying attention to the topsoil they were losing and what they had done to the river. One hundred years of intensive agriculture has taken its toll.

Within eighty years of opening the Twin Falls tract, farmers had washed away the best of their topsoil as irrigation runoff carried it into the river. Studies done by David Carter, a soil scientist at a U.S. Department of Agriculture research station in Kimberly, showed the loss of topsoil reduced potential productivity by an average of about 25 percent. Crop yields dropped to an average of about 75 percent of what they might have been. Dramatic support of Carter's conclusion came in a 1991 University of Idaho study, showing that every day during the irrigation season an average of 350 tons of topsoil washed into the Snake River. The sediments turned runoff the color of café au lait, plainly visible from the Snake River Canyon rim as muddy plumes entering the river.

An acre of topsoil one inch deep weighs about one hundred fifty tons and takes about thirty years to form. Irrigated lands in the Snake River Basin lose an average of nearly nine tons per acre per year--some areas as high as fifteen tons per acre. The math is inevitable. Unless the trend is reversed, southern Idaho will end up like formerly irrigated empires in the Middle East, Africa, southern Europe and Mesopotamia, where five thousand years of irrigation have left dry, unproductive ground with little topsoil.

Silt laden agricultural run-off discolors the Snake River near Twin Falls.

The Snake River carried most of the topsoil downstream. But a substantial portion, over the years, has settled to the river bottom north and west of Twin Falls where return flows entered the river and deposited their silt. It formed extensive deltas that now support their own ecosystems. In places it has made the river shallow and allowed aquatic weeds to flourish.

Irrigation water returns to the river in thirty big canals or streams and twenty smaller ones from more than two hundred thousand acres from the Twin Falls Canal Company and 160,000 acres from the North Side Canal Company. From June 1990 through July 1991, the nine largest tributaries contributed fifty-three thousand tons of sediment. Eighteen other irrigation returns and ten fish hatcheries contributed twenty-seven thousand tons. Together they dumped as much as eighty thousand tons of solids into the river annually. Most of those solids are swept downstream. But enough settle to the bottom to create problems.

The University of Idaho study showed that the river carried about three thousand tons of sediments, averaged over a year, as it reached Milner Dam. It carried about seventy thousand tons as it left the reach at King Hill downstream of the Twin Falls tract. That means an estimated thirteen thousand tons settled to the bottom of the river.

Water quality studies clearly point to irrigated agriculture as the largest, but not the only, contributor of sediments to the river. Runoff from half a million acres of agricultural lands, more than 500 dairies and feedlots, more than 140 fish hatcheries, effluent from food processing plants and municipal sewage treatment plants all discharge into the Snake River. During the irrigation season, Milner Dam blocks the river, and nearly all the water is diverted onto farmlands. Below the dam, the river that once ran clean is recharged with this runoff and other discharges. Springs in the canyon add some clean water, but hydroelectric plants slow the current and let the polluted discharges stew in the warm sunshine, leaving the once mighty river overloaded with pollutants, a weed-choked shadow of its former self.

Some of the stuff that most people think of as pollutants, however, is really pretty nutritious. Waste water from farms, dairies and fish hatcheries carries particles of organic matter and dissolved organic chemicals. Most nutrients critical to plant growth are usually abundant, but availability of nitrogen and phosphorus effectively regulates growth: When nitrogen and phosphorus are plentiful, so is plant growth. Almost half of the nitrogen in the sediments that wash into the river comes from alfalfa crops that are plowed under. Other sources include animal wastes, chemical fertilizers, decayed plant material, as well as septic systems and effluents from waste water treatment systems.

Phosphorus, which also is required for plants to flourish, is usually the least abundant nutrient. That means controlling or reducing the amount of phosphorus in the water effectively limits plant growth. Phosphorus is present in the minerals that make up the inorganic part of the soil, and it also is added as part of chemical fertilizer. Because phosphorus sticks to soil particles, irrigated agriculture contributes a substantial part of the phosphorus in the river. State environmental officials recommended a limit of .05 to .1 milligrams of phosphorus per liter of water to control aquatic weeds. Tests showed phosphorus averaged .24 milligrams per liter in irrigation return flows; .1 milligrams per liter in trout hatchery effluent; and .08 milligrams per liter in the river itself. A hatchery scientist said phosphorus levels as low as .03 milligrams per liter would be enough to spur algae growth.

Nitrogen also seeps into the groundwater and flows into the river along with eroded sediments. Other nutrients also are leached into groundwater with excess irrigation water, and nutrients erode from fields left bare through the winter. Spring thaw and rains can carry off twenty or more tons of soil per acre.

Once in the river, these sediments and nutrients are deposited wherever the current slows. As these materials build up over the years, the waterway gradually becomes a swamp or marsh. Some nutrients are dissolved in the water. These nutrients, especially phosphorus, speed the growth of aquatic plants. The plants block sunlight and, by slowing the water, contribute to further deposits of sediments. When the plants die, the decay process uses oxygen dissolved in the water, reducing the amount available to fish and other aquatic species. The dead plants contribute to the nutrients and sediments on the river bottom. The sediments on the bottom choke off the supply of oxygen to bottom dwelling organisms that many fish feed on, and they cover the gravel that many fish use to spawn. Clean gravel provides secure hiding places for fish eggs while still allowing fresh water to flow past. Too much silt, however, chokes the eggs.

Though no specific statistics are available, grazing, timber harvest and recreation on public lands also contribute to the sediments and bacteria in the streams that feed the Snake River.

Hydropower projects also contribute to poor water quality by trapping nutrients and sediments in reservoirs behind dams. Above the dams, as currents slow, water drops its sediments. The water temperature in the reservoirs rises, changing the aquatic species in the river and reducing the amount of dissolved oxygen the water can hold. Below the hydroelectric dams, quickly changing releases change the physical characteristics of the river, contribute to bank erosion and alter the aquatic habitat. And because they block the river, dams also reduce the effectiveness of high flows that in a natural river scour the river bed during spring runoff and other high water flows.

Officials from the Idaho Department of Environmental Quality have never totaled the amount of pollution that annually runs into the Snake River, but it has good information on many of the tributary streams. Typically these tributaries contribute sediments to the Snake River. The sediments contain inorganic matter as well as the two nutrients essential to plant growth. But most of the nutrients are deposited on the stream bottom where it meets the slack water backed up by the canal company's own Milner Dam and Idaho Power Company's hydroelectric plants on the river. Bacteria from animal feces in runoff from dairies and feedlots at times in the 1990s exceeded state public safety limits for swimming in local creeks. But warnings about unsafe water were rarely posted.

The worst examples included:

* Deep Creek, a few miles west of Twin Falls drains about 36,075 acres and contributed more than five thousand tons of sediments as well as nutrients and bacteria. Nutrients often exceeded recommended limits, and bacteria were traced primarily to livestock, but also intermittent contamination with human wastes.

* Mud Creek, west of Twin Falls, drains about 23,920 acres and contributed 3,600 tons of sediments. Nutrients exceeded state limits and bacteria in the creek were traced to livestock and human wastes.

* Perrine Coulee, drains more than 22,000 acres and contributed more than seven thousand tons of sediments.

Pollution problems got so bad that in the dry summers of the 1990s mats of algae and aquatic weeds blanketed the Snake River. Ducks and muskrats scampered across the river on the green mush and coots built nests on it. A muskrat was seen napping on one algae mat near Thousand Springs. A little farther downstream, three great blue herons stood on a mat that floated like a football-field-sized island in the middle of the river. Along the bank; grebes built nests on the thick green tangle. In some places the algae kept canoeists and water-skiers off the river. And sometimes tourists canceled their reservations to find cleaner waters elsewhere. The main component of those green mats was the aquatic weeds rooted in sediments in shallow, slow moving water. They trapped floating algae, and when uprooted they floated downstream in long mats, some up to one-half mile long. They were a good indication of just how bad the water quality problems were in the river.

In September 1990, state officials listed the Snake River below Milner Dam as a "water quality limited segment," meaning that portion of the river violated state and federal water quality standards. Nutrients exceeded recommended limits, especially during June, July and August. Bacteria levels exceeded water quality standards most of the time. Federal environmental law forced the state to develop a plan to improve water quality by limiting the amount of pollutants entering the river every day.

The following spring, on a warm and sunny afternoon, then-Governor Cecil Andrus came down from Boise to get a firsthand look at the problem in the river. He got a dramatic demonstration. As he was touring the river with state and federal environmental officials, his boat was waylaid by the very problem he had come to inspect. Floating algae plugged the jet boat's intakes, leaving the governor and the environmental officials bobbing helplessly in mid-river. "I wanted to see firsthand the middle Snake," Andrus said. "We saw a very ill river." The governor clambered aboard another boat and returned to shore.

He got what he came for, and perhaps a little more.

He saw that the river was plagued by stagnation, siltation and algae growth, and that it needed protection. The problem was worse after a string of drier than average years, when the current was not enough to help flush some of the algae downstream. But more water was not the answer. That would just send the problem downstream to bigger reservoirs. Even in wet years, the algae growth showed the river had problems. The river's ills were the result of too many years of more sediments, nutrients and bacteria than the river could handle. The state and the water users could no longer just discharge their wastes into the river heedless of any effect. They would have to stop contaminants before they reached the river. It was time to account for nearly a century of destructive agricultural practices.

Not just the loss of topsoil and productivity inspired the farmers of the Twin Falls tract to get involved in cleaning up their discharges in the 1990s. If they didn't, the federal Environmental Protection Agency would force the state to clean up the mess. The 1972 Clean Water Act imposes discharge restrictions on "point pollution sources," pollution that can be traced to a specific point, such as a pipe or ditch. Though canal companies discharge runoff from a ditch, the act lumped them with other agricultural "nonpoint pollution," which is considered general runoff from a wide area, such as fields or pastures. Nonpoint pollution is the source of 90 percent of the pollutants in the southern Idaho waters but is exempt from state and federal pollution discharge regulations. As a result, largely unregulated agricultural runoff has affected hundreds of miles of streams in Idaho and across the West. The difference also exempted canal companies from direct regulation. Irrigators and canal companies were required only to follow best management practices.

With the water quality problems in the Snake River and the ongoing efforts to do something about it, many farmers, including Twin Falls Canal Company leaders, began to realize that if they didn't clean up their discharges on their own, the state or the federal government would step in to force changes. They recognized the possibility that Congress could change the definition of point source pollution to include the discharges from irrigated agriculture. That would force the canal companies into the federal National Pollution Discharge Elimination System, essentially an industrial permitting program with strict discharge limits. Without a permit, a canal company could be forced to stop discharging. That wouldn't necessarily halt all farming on the Twin Falls tract, but it would certainly make things more difficult. "We'd rather be part of the solution than have a mandate come and say, 'This is it,'" said Bob Schaer, a former president of the Twin Falls Canal Company board.

The effort began slowly. In the early 1970s, the North Side Canal Company, which had more trouble with erosion, started digging settling ponds in its major return flows to capture some of the sediment in runoff before it got into the river. The Twin Falls Canal Company soon followed suit.

The canal companies also got some help from a federally funded pilot project started in 1977 by the Natural Resources Conservation Service—formerly the Soil Conservation Service. One of the worst erosion problems on the Twin Falls project was the return flow channel known as the "LQ Drain," which carries sediment-laden runoff from fields north of Filer back to the Snake River. The project showed farmers that trapping topsoil and the nutrients it contains and returning it to the fields would soon pay for itself. And it would keep a lot of sediment out of the river. Another Conservation Service demonstration project, from 1981 through 1990, helped farmers along Rock Creek dig settling ponds and plant grass filter strips along the edges of fields to keep sediments out of the creek. The project showed a marked reduction in sediment and bacteria levels in Rock Creek.

By the late 1990s, the Twin Falls and North Side canal companies were making a serious effort at capturing sediments in the runoff with settling ponds and some of the other methods farmers had been learning from the Conservation Service.

Brian Olmstead didn't need help from the federal government to realize the value of keeping the topsoil on his fields, where it belonged. That's something his father taught him. To stem the tide of eroding soil, Olmstead dug ponds on all the drains on his farm to trap sediment that washed from his fields. "I don't think we knew how much we were losing until we put it in a pond," he said. He can usually find someone willing to dig a pond if he lets them keep the dirt. One pond near his house has a small island, where ducks nest in the cattails. He spreads the soil he recovers back on his fields to fill low spots. Some of it comes off neighbors' fields. "If there's a stream running through my place, I like to run it through a pond first," he said.

As water from an irrigation ditch flows across the field it picks up silt from the bare ground. By the time it is about a third of the way across the field it has picked up as much as it can carry. That's why the top part of many fields looks lighter; the topsoil is gone and the farmer has plowed up the lighter-colored subsoil, which is far less productive. More than one foot of top soil already is gone from most fields on the Twin Falls tract.

To be effective, a pond must be large enough that it takes water at least one hour to pass through. When water slows down that much, most of the sediment will settle out. When the idea for the ponds first surfaced, the Twin Falls Canal Company's reaction was that it didn't have enough land to put in wetlands or settling ponds. But since its initial experimental efforts, the company realized it didn't need large areas, and it now has put in several ponds on company drains. The system is full of small wild areas of an acre or less, which are too irregular to be farmed easily. Canal company employees now scour the system for those little pieces that can be turned into ponds or wetlands. Some are just pieces of steep ground near a coulee where a dam at one end would raise the water level. In other places, where there is room, an area is simply excavated to form a pond. The canal company also encourages landowners to put in their own conservation measures to keep more of the topsoil on their own land.

Settling ponds, some of which may look suspiciously like wetlands, can reduce sediments from irrigation waste water by up to 80 percent. But just as important, they show a commitment to improve water quality. And the ponds demonstrate to local farmers how much of their soil they're really losing. Many are surprised when they see the amount collected by a settling pond.

Chuck Coiner, a canal company board member and a Republican state legislator who farms east of Twin Falls, put in his first settling pond more than twenty-five years ago. Since then he has added five acres to one of his fields by filling a sloping corner with soil captured in a settling pond. The soil came from water that ran off his neighbors' fields. Now all his fields drain into ponds to capture eroded topsoil. He spreads it back on his fields or uses it to build up other low spots and grade the slope of fields.

Despite the obvious benefits, however, building and cleaning out the ponds is expensive. It would be better to leave the soil on the fields. Leaving organic matter in the soil helps hold it, and not overworking the ground reduces erosion. But some farmers work the soil more than it needs, and that means more erosion.

Like most farmers, Olmstead doesn't like to do more work than necessary. He would rather keep the soil on the field where it belongs. To reduce erosion he plows as little as possible, a method known as "conservation tillage," which reduces the amount of soil disturbance and leaves organic material in the soil to help hold it. He also uses crop rotation where he can, and sprinklers where possible and on steeper fields. Where those alternatives don't work, he applies a chemical known as polyacrilamide, or PAM, which binds to the soil in the water and helps reduce erosion. Keeping the topsoil where it belongs shows up in better yields from his crops. Olmstead says soil conservation would save farmers money in the long term. It also would keep a lot of sediment out of the river.

Olmstead's ponds used to fill up every year, but now with careful management and conservation tillage it takes two to three years for them to fill in with silt. Crop rotation helps. But the way sugar beets and beans are grown means bare dirt will be exposed to irrigation water before the root masses develop to help hold the soil. He uses sprinklers on those kinds of crops on any land that's more than 2 percent slope. He also has put in filter strips—twenty feet or more of grass or spring grain crops across the end of a field—to slow runoff and filter out silt before water leaves the field. Grains and hay fields, however, don't present erosion problems. The plants are much closer together, and their root systems hold soil well.

Increasingly, other farmers are learning and using the same methods Olmstead uses to trap their topsoil before it goes into the river. The effort has reduced erosion by 35 percent.

One October morning in 2000, several farmers, Twin Falls Canal Company officials and environmental officials set off down the river in a pair of inflatable rafts and two canoes. Brian Olmstead, who had taken a job as the canal company's field supervisor, wanted them to see those return flows when they're running clean and the effects the sediments have had on the river all these years. He also wanted to show them the results of their efforts to reduce erosion from their fields. By the end of the irrigation season in 2000, the canal company had seventy-five settling ponds. The group set off from the spot where Rock Creek enters the Snake River, northwest of the city of Twin Falls. Olmstead and other company officials, board members and farmers donned life jackets and climbed aboard the rafts and canoes.

Four-hundred-foot canyon walls rose above the pea green

river and the ash trees in their golden fall regalia. The mud along the banks of the Snake River down here was once topsoil on the farms above the canyon rim. The 350 tons of sediment runoff a day during the height of the irrigation season had been reduced by at least one-third by the late 1990s. But it doesn't take much to muddy an otherwise clean return, Olmstead noted. Only one farmer in ten not making an effort to keep sediments out of the runoff can mask the efforts of the rest. And canal company and state officials had little regulatory authority — other than peer pressure — to clean up the sediments.

A boat-load of farmers heads down the Snake River to observe the results of their erosion control efforts.

Paddles dipped lazily as the current carried the group slowly past the panorama of lush riparian wetlands and sheer basalt cliffs beneath a warm sun and high thin clouds. They beached the rafts and canoes on the mud where Lateral 30 leaps off the canyon rim south of Filer and runs into the Snake River. During high water, sediments carried by this return flow have created a small delta where the stream meets the river. When the river level drops, the stream cuts down through the silt and carries it into the river, creating a miniature canyon and a plume of sediments farmers could see for themselves. Once bare mud, the delta now supports trees, willows and thick underbrush.

Brian Olmstead checks two water quality samples from the Snake River.

Deer, birds, raccoons and other small animals had left their tracks in the soft mud. This was topsoil washed down by one of the toughest return flows to clean up, Olmstead said. Using a quart-sized glass "Imhoff cone," Olmstead scooped up a sample of water from the stream. The tan sediment settled to the cone's narrow bottom, where marks etched on the glass represent milligrams of sediment in a liter of water. In 1990 the average amount of sediment from Lateral 30 was 136 milligrams per liter of water. By 1998, it had dropped to less than 100 milligrams. On this October day it showed about 25 milligrams, well below the goal of 52 milligrams.

The last stop was Lateral 39/39A, which had looked like Nestle's Quik earlier in the season. A young golden eagle circled above the floaters and landed in a hole high in the north canyon wall. During the irrigation season, Olmstead measured more than seventeen hundred milligrams per liter in this return flow. Then, in late summer, the company built a settling pond on the lateral above the canyon rim, too late to show any real effect that year. But on that October day the Imhoff cone showed it carried well below the fifty-two milligram limit.

The float trip showed the farmers that erosion and deposition are natural processes, but agriculture speeds them up by clearing topsoil of natural plant cover, annual plowing and irrigation. The canal company can do only so much to meet the goals and clean up the river; to be effective, all irrigators must contribute, Olmstead said. To force all its members to do their part, the company changed its bylaws to require irrigators to meet company discharge standards for water that leaves their fields.

The rafts and canoes maneuvered to avoid running aground on submerged rocks as the current swung them around. No one fell in the water. Farther along, a great blue heron rose with a prehistoric squawk from its roost in a willow tree, a belted kingfisher raced past like there was somewhere it just had to be. The farmers were encouraged to see that their efforts were beginning to have an effect. Many had never been down on the river in all the years they had farmed the lands above.

"I'm encouraged by what I saw in those return flows," Castleford farmer Mike Bulkley said, as he helped drag a raft up on shore.

Chapter Eleven:
Company Trapper

One February day in the early 1990s, Larry Finney parked his pickup truck by a small irrigation ditch to check a floating muskrat trap. He scrambled back up the canal bank and threw a dead muskrat in the back of the pickup to join about a dozen more he already had gathered from his trap line that morning. That would have made a good day's wage in the days when pelts still were worth $7 each, he groused. But Finney didn't have to depend on pelts to make his living. He is the company trapper for the Twin Falls Canal Company. His job is to keep down the numbers of rodents and other small animals, especially muskrats, that threaten the integrity of the company's canals by burrowing into the canal banks. He deals with perhaps the most important of several unintended results of creating artificial rivers and pouring large amounts of water on land that rarely saw more than twelve inches of precipitation in an entire year.

The irrigation system that made crops possible also created ideal habitat for numerous species of animals and plants that in turn caused problems for the canal system. Burrowing animals arrived soon after the first water ran in these canals, and like wear-and-tear and breakdowns, they have been coming back every year. But they are only one of the many problems that came with the water when the farmers began to irrigate the desert. The challenges that faced canal company operators in maintaining a dependable water supply included controlling threats to system integrity and dealing with emergencies. Some problems they anticipated, but others were unforeseen, and the irrigators had to learn as they went. Despite the problems, the farmers and the canal company never saw their endeavor as a battle to conquer nature. They recognized that the canal system always would require maintenance, and the natural systems that allowed farms to flourish also brought animals and plants. Balancing the needs of the farmers and controlling natural threats to the system that supplied them would mean establishing and maintaining a long-standing relationship with nature. And most realize the tenuous nature of that balance.

One of the earliest problems to plague the farmers was unforeseen and had nothing to do with opportunistic plants or animals. In some places, the water interacted with underground features, causing it to appear in unexpected places. Irrigators worry about too little water, but suddenly the problem was too much water. The system engineers and irrigators expected water seeping into the ground to flow underground into the river, and in some places it did, like at the Thousand Springs on the north side of the river. But in a few places on the western half of the tract, the water hit a solid, impermeable hardpan. The water table began to rise, up to thirty feet in some places, and suddenly began to flow from springs where springs had never flowed before. Or the water simply stood in the fields. By 1911, parts of the project were waterlogged. Attempts at digging drainage channels had limited success. By the 1920s, thousands of acres were too wet to farm.

At first farmers whose sodden fields were unusable paid half the cost of the crews who dug the channels. When it became apparent that it would require much more effort, the canal company eventually took on the expense, to be shared among all the shareholders.

An attempt to blast drain holes in the Rock Creek Canyon wall backfired, driving the water to the surface instead. The company next hired a well driller to punch a six-inch hole into the rock beneath the surface. The drill went down ninety-five feet before it bit into hard clay. When the surface water disappeared, the company decided to try drilling more drain wells in other wet areas. In 1918 the company bought four drilling rigs. The wells worked and soon were common in all waterlogged areas. Northwest of Filer, farmers installed fifteen-inch drain tile in their fields that speeded up drainage for hundreds of acres. By the 1920s, 290 miles of drains had dried up 65,000 acres.

In 1924, crews with jackhammers and drills went to work on the southwest wall of Rock Creek Canyon. The men packed dynamite into the twenty-foot-deep holes, and set it off. Water started gushing out of the canyon wall. Crews also started working on a series of tunnels, fifty feet below the surface. Other tunnels 100 feet deep lowered the water table through drainage wells. These tunnels helped drain much of the tract. At first they cost about $7.50 per foot. By 1948 the cost had gone up to $27.50 per foot. In all, forty-nine tunnels were dug, two of them more than a mile long.

Courtesy Twin Falls Canal Co.
Workers dig a drainage trench

The canal company spent about $2 million on drainage, but some of the water could be recovered and used elsewhere for additional irrigation. In some areas, where tunnels had been dug or drainage tile installed, a few new springs appeared. The water was put back to work irrigating more land or run through ponds to raise fish. Though poor drainage was only a serious problem in parts of the tract, aquatic plants created problems everywhere. Canal water carried plants and seeds that took root. A variety of algae and aquatic plant species are lumped under the inclusive term "moss." Long, sinuous tendrils of green waved in the current, and cattails, sedges and reeds took root in the shallows. Together these plants grew to choke smaller laterals and to interfere with water delivery.

In 1918, the canal company adapted a disk harrow drawn by two horses, one on each side of the canal, to uproot weeds in the canals. Some would use a heavy chain, like a ship's anchor chain, one end on each side of the canal and dragged along the same way by two horses or by a pair of tractors. The process was company manager Vince Alberdi's introduction to canal system operations. During high school he worked summers "mossing" the canals and laterals of the North Side Canal Company. The company and other irrigation companies also use chemicals, most commonly Magnacide H and xylene. But these are dangerous. After xylene got into a private drinking water well near Rupert, and after a Twin Falls Canal Company employee died from complications associated with exposure to Magnacide H, many irrigators reduced or eliminated their reliance on chemicals, and went back to tractors and chains.

Once the weeds are loosened, they float down to the next downstream obstruction, where workers with pitchforks scoop them out into piles. In some places with lots of plant material, a modern backhoe or a larger track-hoe is required. Aquatic plants in a favorable environment will always be a problem, just like the small animals Finney traps — some of which thrive on those aquatic weeds.

A smile comes easily to Finney's weathered face. And why not? He earns his living doing what he would otherwise do on his time off. Early attempts to halt erosion of canal banks by lining them with sagebrush may have helped some. But by also improving muskrat and beaver habitat, the effort created a whole new series of problems. Controlling the number of burrowing animals, whose burrows threaten the integrity of the canal banks, is a full-time job and an important part of keeping the system intact. A canal break in 1988 was the result of a badger hole. Two breaks in 1986 were attributed to ground squirrels, and two more in 1978 may have been caused by muskrats. But because private trappers worked only when pelt prices made it worth the effort, the canal company decided to hire a full-time company trapper.

Finney grew up hunting around his parents' farm near the Salmon Falls Creek Canyon in the Hollister and Rogerson area west and south of the Twin Falls tract. He has been trapping for money since sheepherders started paying him a bounty on coyotes when he was about twelve. He began trapping for the canal company in 1979, and now his most frequent and numerous quarry is the muskrat, an aquatic rodent of about the size of a small house cat. He sells the pelts to supplement his salary. When fur prices are up, Finney gets help from other trappers. Muskrat fur is used for coats, and in Japan and France for making small, furry toys. But when prices are low, few are interested in trapping, and muskrat numbers climb.

Muskrats are prolific breeders that often have two litters a year, with three to nine young in each litter. With soft and woolly dark brown fur, they look like a small beaver with a long, scaly oval tail and webbed hind feet. They favor alfalfa when they can get it, but they also eat freshwater mussels and crayfish as well as cattails, water lily and other riparian plants that also annoy the canal company. In fact, in some other places muskrats are used to control aquatic weeds. Their numbers grow quickly in favorable habitat. They dig dens in canal banks, with the entrance often under water. The burrow curves four to six feet into the bank and up to a large single nest chamber above the waterline. Muskrats also threaten the narrower lateral banks that carry water from the canals to fields. That's a particular danger where laterals wind along the side of a hill. A break in the downhill side could wash out fields and roads.

Over one winter, Finney trapped sixteen hundred "rats," as he calls them. A year earlier, he had trapped 750 of the aquatic rodents, along with forty-three badgers, five beavers and countless squirrels. His traps sometimes catch skunks, mink, porcupine and the occasional coyote. Ground squirrels also dig tunnels in the banks. They are smaller, but their primary threat is that they attract badgers and fox, which dig for the squirrels. Badgers are prodigious diggers and present the biggest threat. They dig their own burrows by enlarging squirrel or muskrat tunnels. If a badger hole coming in from the dry side meets a muskrat hole from the wet side, the result could wash out a section of canal bank.

The money the canal company pays Finney is well spent, Alberdi says. When full, the canal system holds billions of gallons of water uphill from thousands of homes and farms. One hungry badger can risk the millions of dollars at stake in crops and canal banks. With the system at full capacity, animal burrows that were exposed earlier may be underwater, and a small hole all the way through the bank can quickly become a big hole.

Sometimes it's surprising how little it takes to cause a canal break. With canal banks lining more than a hundred miles of main canals and more than one thousand miles of laterals, the record is really pretty good. Most years the canal company sees a few minor leaks and maybe one good-sized leak. Big, serious leaks don't happen every year, but water working through a small hole can, over time, erode into a serious leak. Or the simple cooling and warming of an empty pipe under the canal during the winter can create a void between the pipe and the soil. When the canal is refilled in the spring, the water can find the void and follow it down along the pipe, resulting in a serious leak.

In July 1991, crew member Lynn Stephens was cleaning a lateral when he noticed water where there wasn't supposed to be any. It was leaking from the Low Line Canal southwest of Twin Falls. He called in the break, and repair crews streamed to the site like beavers rushing to a leak in their dams. The crews worked through the night. The leak from the base of a canal bank soaked nearby fields and covered local roads. It had started at about four cubic feet per second about 4 p.m. But by the time the crews isolated the leak and got a temporary cofferdam in place, the flow had grown to about 150 cubic feet. Water had started leaking along a metal drain pipe that ran under the canal. The crews went home after they got the leak stopped at about 3:30 a.m. The next day, crews dug out the damaged section and rebuilt the canal bank.

Still the most common cause of leaks is burrowing animals. One day in May 1995, the residents of Hansen, a small town east of Twin Falls, thought a muskrat or badger had caused a canal break as water rose in the streets, trapping patrons in the South Hills Saloon. The alarm sent Alberdi to the canal company's safety valve near Hansen. Point Spill is about ten miles east of Twin Falls, where the main canal swings out near the canyon. Here the main canal at peak flow carries 3,600 cubic feet per second or 1.6 million gallons of water per minute. Raising the gates in an emergency can spill most of that.

The original structure had been built with the rest of the system in 1905. Concern over whether it would hold up to perform its vital function as a safety valve led the company to rebuild it in

1994. Two new radial gates were set in concrete within spitting distance of the canyon—each gate is eighteen feet wide and eleven feet high. During a test, the new gates rose with the quiet whine of electric motors. A sheet of water shot from the gap and plummeted through a steel culvert and down a rock-lined channel that only an instant ago had been dry. Finally, it shot over the canyon rim. The artificial waterfall, created at the touch of a button, this day released only two hundred cubic feet per second. The capacity of the structure is much more than that, but because of heavy rains, water in the canal already had been cut back upstream.

The report of a break in the main canal was a false alarm—Alberdi's favorite kind. The problem wasn't a canal break after all. Heavy rainfall had simply caused some local flooding. At the touch of a switch, the gates slid closed again, cutting off the stream of water just like turning off a bathtub faucet. When the rain slowed, the flooding subsided, and the saloon patrons could return home.

Most of Larry Finney's days start with a phone call from a farmer or ditch rider reporting muskrats, a badger digging in a canal bank, or a fox digging in the High Line Canal. He puts a lot of miles on the muddy four-wheel-drive company pickup truck, chasing calls over the 350-square-mile tract.

During the winter, when most of the system is dry, the year-round streams in the west end of the tract become a refuge for muskrats. In one stretch of stream—about one-tenth of a mile—Finney had trapped about forty rats only halfway through one winter. His floating traps are baited with a concoction he cooks up at home. He starts with an extract from muskrat scent glands that give the critter its name. He adds anything else that stinks—a mixture of catnip, molasses, urine from a female coyote in heat, maybe a little sturgeon fat. The traps kill the rats quickly, Finney said.

Finney is sensitive to criticism of his trapping, shooting or poisoning small furry animals lured by the manmade habitat. A pair of dusty, well-worn .22-caliber rifles hang from a rifle rack in the pickup cab. He uses them to quickly dispatch animals caught in his traps, and he figures he fires maybe ten thousand rounds in a year. He regrets the occasional weasel in his traps. Weasels are his ally. They hunt mice and ground squirrels, and they don't dig their own burrows. But it's one of the costs of creating such an artificial environment, which also can spring some surprises.

All the things that can cause canals to leak, will, and at the worst possible time; and not all of them are caused by animals. One day, two canal workers were walking along the bottom of an empty canal, chatting as they went. One of them turned to say something to the other. But he was gone. He heard a voice, but his companion was gone. The voice called again, seeming from below. There he was, only his head showing on the bottom of the dry canal bed. He had stepped into a sinkhole, the bane of southern Idaho canal companies. He was unhurt and quickly rescued by his friend. The hole was filled. But others like it occasionally open as water erodes voids in the fractured basalt that underlies the surface.

In November 1996, one such hole opened in the main canal about a mile and a half downstream from the diversion gates at Milner Dam. The hole was so big, it reversed the flow in the canal. Ditch rider Bob Schaer noticed the water flowing the wrong way in the canal, and tracked it to the gaping hole about thirty feet long and ten feet wide. Luckily, the irrigation season was over, and the flow already had been shut off. The hole drained only a few remaining feet of mostly slack water. But in the hole, the bottom dropped away to darkness. Stones dropped into the abyss rattled for a couple of seconds.

Such holes open every year or two. But nobody could remember one this big. The causes remain uncertain, and may include earthquakes and erosion. Workers opened the crack and filled it with bentonite clay, tamped it down and regraded the canal bed.

Finney runs a year-round badger trap line at the edge of the irrigated tract to keep the prodigious diggers out of the system. Badgers are built low to the ground, broad-backed and flattened looking, with strong claws built for digging. They are grizzled brown and white with a long, bushy tail and a longitudinal stripe from their upturned weasel snout back across their heads to their powerful shoulders. Second only to the wolverine in the weasel family, badgers have sharp carnivore teeth and an uncompromising attitude. Badgers have few enemies and a ferocious reputation. They don't back down—not even from rattlesnakes. Apparently they are immune to the snake's venom, or perhaps their fur is simply too thick for the fangs to penetrate. That thick fur on neck and shoulders also provides good protection against dogs and coyotes. Though they shuffle with an awkward swagger, badgers can move with surprising speed. They live in sagebrush plains from Mexico to southwestern Canada, and from the Pacific Coast to the Midwest. They raise their young in dry, grass-lined dens two to three feet below the ground. And they prey heavily on ground squirrels and gophers. A badger can out-dig them underground, overtaking them in an excavation race.

Badgers dig their dens by enlarging existing holes of fox or ground squirrels. The tunnels are oval to match the badger's low-slung profile, about eight inches high by twelve inches wide.

Badgers are pretty tough.

"He'll whip a coyote and walk off," Finney said. He has been bitten and scratched more than once trying to free from his traps nearly every kind of animal found in southern Idaho. Once he had to carry a coyote back to the truck, where he kept his rifle, because it had clamped onto his hand and wouldn't let go. But his worst injury was self-inflicted. An angry badger had gotten hold of his pant leg, and Finney couldn't convince it to let go. He decided to try to hit it with his irrigation shovel. He took a big swing at the critter. He missed and smashed himself in the shin. Impressed with Finney's ferocity, the badger finally let go and lumbered off unhurt. Finney limped back to his truck, cursing all badgers. He keeps a wary eye on them. Though they don't reach the numbers of muskrats, they still are a formidable threat to the canal system. A badger can dig through a canal bank in fifteen minutes.

Part Three: The Law

Swan Falls Dam on the Snake River south of Boise

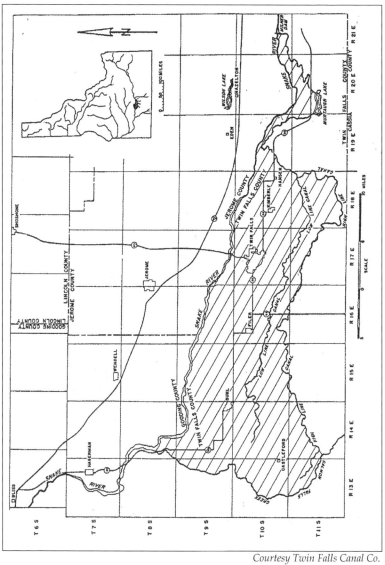

Shaded area: Lands irrigated by the Twin Falls Canal Company.

Chapter Twelve:
Water rights

Ten years before the Twin Falls Land and Water Company started construction on Milner Dam at The Cedars, someone already had started diverting water from the Snake River about nine miles upstream. Henry Schodde, born in Berlin, Germany, in 1851, came west in the 1870s and began diverting water to his homestead along the river in 1883. He built eleven large, wooden water wheels that used the force of the current to raise water to irrigate about 160 acres on the north side of the river and 264 acres on the south side. The wheels varied in height from twenty-four to thirty-four feet, and buckets attached to the wheels raised the water as much as twenty feet from the river to his fields. Wing dams raised the river and directed the flow so the current would drive the wheels. His water rights totaled twenty-five cubic feet per second and dated from 1889 and 1895. The crops he raised fed a herd of cows he had brought up from Nevada.

Construction of Milner Dam raised the river level and all but stopped the current, rendering Schodde's water wheels impotent. He filed a lawsuit for $56,650 in damages in 1905. He argued that the current, being necessary for his water wheels to function, was part of his water right. The court did not agree. He had a claim only on the water and not on the current. In 1908, a federal appeals court and subsequently the U.S. Supreme Court in 1912 rejected his argument as well. "It is conceded and is beyond question, that the statute law as well as judicial authority directly protects plaintiff in all the water he has actually appropriated, diverted, and used, but there is no statute, nor, so far as known, any judicial rulings, protecting him in the establishment and in the use of his water wheels, as he claims to, and must, use them for the diversion of water to his land," the Supreme Court wrote, quoting the lower court.

An appropriation of water is not unrestricted but must consider the rights of the public. Schodde was one of the first in the area to use the Snake River for irrigation, but his senior water right didn't include an absolute right to the means or method of diversion, and he had made no appropriation of the current. His was the first legal challenge to the Twin Falls Canal Company's right to divert water from the river. An earlier challenge was directed at a hydro-power diversion at Shoshone Falls and aimed to protect the scenic beauty of the falls. But it might have blocked the canal company's diversion as well, had it not been resolved.

Schodde's case foretold the complexity of water law in southern Idaho and only hinted at the thorny issues that would arise among the competing water users along the Snake River. Schodde learned the hard way, as would others in time, that being first was not necessarily enough. His water right and the canal company's right to use water from the river existed only in context of other rights and other water users. Like any water user, Schodde or the canal company would only have water as long as others respected their water rights or the water user could convince a court to force them to leave the water in the river. Enforcing the law often has been hampered by the reluctance of officials to turn off water to a farmer; some irrigators refused, to the point of violence, to shut off their diversions when their water ran out. That was especially true in dry years. And sometimes it was hard to tell who had the right to how much water. Adding reservoirs to store the heavy spring runoff extended the supply to carry through dry years, but also added complexity. It was hard to explain to a farmer whose crop was withering for lack of irrigation why he was not entitled to the water running right past his closed head gates to users downstream.

Ultimately, water users on the Snake River in eastern and southern Idaho—upstream of Milner Dam—began to realize that the complexity of the system required some kind of organization among them. Cooperation was the only way to make the system work for all water users. Most eventually, and a few reluctantly, accepted the idea of cooperative management of the river and the storage reservoirs. They soon found that cooperation allowed more flexibility and more efficient use of scarce water in the arid region. That did not end water fights, but it provided a forum to work out most disagreements. Some still ended up in court.

The state's water laws, which helped govern the orderly administration of water, were based on the assumption that water belongs to the people of the state. Water rights don't confer ownership of water, they allow only the right to use it, a concept known as "usufruct." Such rights to use water were granted on an order of seniority. The first to use water for a recognized "beneficial use" retained the senior right to use a reasonable amount of water before other, more junior rights were allowed any water. Like most other water users along the river, the Twin Falls Land and Water Company—and subsequently the investors that became the Twin Falls Canal Company—had substantial investments that depended on the right to divert and use a "reasonable" amount of water from the river. Without that water right, the investment in the construction, the clearing of land and the planting of crops would mean nothing.

Schodde and the canal company, though on opposite sides of that early challenge, both counted on the principle known as prior appropriation to defend their water rights. Idaho water law is based on the principle that the earliest legitimate water users have the first claim to water in times of shortages. This doctrine provided security to those who use the water, as a real property right. The doctrine grew out of English common law—the ideals of open markets and private property that protected water-driven mills from later upstream development. The prior appropriation doctrine carried an aura of fairness. The first person to develop a water resource, as long as he or she is diverting a reasonable amount of water for a reasonable purpose, should not have his or her investment jeopardized by someone who wants to develop a diversion upstream. The concept was first widely used in the West during the California gold rush.

In the gold fields, a utilitarian view of nature teamed with greed to nurture the idea that natural resources were there to profit those who were able to exploit them. In practice, the prior appropriation doctrine was developed to overcome the scarcity of nature by applying technology. And it was used as a tool by early capitalists to profit from public resources, to drive factories and mills on the power of water in the early 1800s. The doctrine allowed the first users to keep control of the water in a river.

"A river became a mere instrumentality to satisfy entrepreneurial drives, a utility, a marketable commodity, to be bought and sold and made to earn money for whoever got there first," Donald Worster said in his book, *Rivers of Empire: Water, Aridity and the Growth of the American West.*

The doctrine protected that utilitarian view. It worked well in arid regions where water was scarce, and soon spread through other western states and territories. Idaho officially adopted prior appropriation as the law in 1881. It established a chronological order of water delivery. Priorities were set by the date a water right was established. Most of the early rights were established simply by putting the water to use. Those older rights have the highest priority: A 1900 water right is senior to a 1903 water right, but junior to an 1898 right. When the stream runs low, the oldest rights get their water before others. Prior appropriation thus forms a bridge between paper water rights and actual water in the stream. And it allows irrigation of lands far from a water source.

The riparian system of water rights, which prevailed in the eastern parts of the country, allowed only those property owners with land adjacent to the river to divert and use the water. But because of the normally ample rainfall, it was of little concern— most had plenty of water. The riparian system did not allow the diversion and transport of water to lands not bordering the stream. In the arid West, however, this principle hampered the development of land that had no water on it or wasn't near any water. Prior appropriation extended irrigation beyond lands adjacent to waterways and allowed the development of lands anywhere it was economically feasible to transport the water. The concept allowed a more complete exploitation of the resource than the riparian system. Prior appropriation allocated water essentially until the river was dry, as is the case at Milner Dam.

By ensuring an orderly and dependable distribution of water, the doctrine allowed farmers to invest in expensive facilities and systems to divert and transport water to land far from the river, without fear that others would take the water once their irrigation systems were complete. Without this doctrine, the Twin Falls Land and Water Company would have been unlikely to find anyone willing to invest in the expensive irrigation system.

But the doctrine also has some flaws. It is based on the assumption that the West should be settled and farmed and that water resources ought to be fully developed and exploited. Implicit in the doctrine is the notion that nature is intended for man's benefit, and full utilization and development of water resources is an improvement on nature. That notion ignores the intangible entity that is the river, which is much more than the sum of the rocks, plants, animals and water.

The doctrine also institutionalizes a system of allocating a public resource that is inherently unfair to outsiders. It gives control over that resource to the state in a system that purports to be a free market economy. The state, not the market, controls the definition of beneficial uses. And the recognized beneficial uses today still largely reflect the values of the nineteenth century. Allowing a stream to flow peacefully, undisturbed or simply to support fish and the aquatic ecosystem, was not among the accepted beneficial uses of the water originally. In recent years, changes have begun to creep into the law, including minimum stream flows and the idea that leaving water in the stream for fish, recreation and aesthetics could be considered beneficial. The state now recognizes the value of protecting water resources for something other than development. But only the state Water Resources Board can hold the rights to an instream flow. Irrigators can't dedicate a portion of their rights to remain in the river. If they did, others could challenge the right, claim forfeiture by lack of use and file a water right of their own on the flow—or it simply would go to the next junior water user.

Idaho's Constitution and water law encourage full economic development of the state's water resources while protecting existing uses. As a result, farmers grow rich using these resources. The people who own the water get nothing, yet when granting new water rights on their behalf, the state requires that the public interest be considered, in addition to preventing injury to existing rights. This "public trust doctrine" requires the state to manage the water resources on behalf of the people and to consider public interests, such as water for fish and wildlife, water quality and recreation, and it obligates the state to protect those public values. The public trust doctrine challenges the notion that irrigation is the highest and best use of water, a notion that still holds sway among many irrigators in southern Idaho. The state Legislature, however, has removed the doctrine in the administration of water rights. The state has defended its administration of water and water rights in the Snake River with the threadbare excuse that the Snake is "a working river."

In the 1880s, Mormon farmers from Utah settled the upper Snake River valley. They built networks of small canals supplied by water diverted from the Snake River and its tributaries. By 1900 they were irrigating more than 200,000 acres. The most common way of diverting water was to build a temporary dam partway across the river using rocks, gravel, brush and canvas, extending the structure farther out into the river as the water level dropped. Most of the structures were washed away by high flows in the spring and rebuilt the following summer.

Those early irrigators adjusted their crops and acreage by estimating the amount of water and snow that fell in the mountains. They raised a lot of hay and grains that grew and matured during the time when plenty of water was available. Wheat ripened about the time the natural flows in the river began to drop. With the abundance of water and little competition, many early farmers didn't bother to register their water rights or the priority date. They simply diverted water as they needed it. And they rarely measured it. So long as the number of farmers remained few and the water remained plentiful with enough for everyone, it was not a problem.

Then in August 1901, the river ran dry at Blackfoot for the first time that anyone could remember. It had been a dry year and precipitation in the headwaters had been lower than usual. But the numbers of irrigators and irrigated acres had continued to grow. In addition, more farmers were raising crops that required more water through the end of the summer and into early fall, beyond the season of plenty.

The specter of drought shattered the commonly held optimism that the Snake River always would exceed irrigation needs. The spirit of cooperation dried up along with the water supply. Farmers would no longer put up with unregulated use. They tried to apply the prior appropriation doctrine to administer the dwindling water supply. But that was hopeless. The prior appropriation doctrine was useless without accurate records. And few of those early farmers had written records of their water rights. The ensuing tangle resulted in a lawsuit and the adjudication of upper valley water rights to unravel their priorities. The process started in 1901 and took ten years to complete.

Meanwhile, crops withered in the hot summer sun near Blackfoot while a few miles upstream canals ran full. Tension among irrigators grew. With the uncertainty of the still-pending decree, upstream farmers were reluctant to let any water go to help their downstream neighbors. The downstream users asked the court for help. In the absence of any clear priority, the judge working on the decree granted them some water. But it was short-term relief, and downstream irrigators were looking beyond the pending decree for a solution. They were convinced storage reservoirs that could capture and store the abundance of spring runoff would provide a more dependable water supply. But they lacked the money and expertise to build reservoirs big enough to make a difference, and upstream farmers, who rarely ran dry, saw no advantage to the reservoirs. So they turned to the federal government for help. The Reclamation Service—created in 1902 and renamed the Bureau of Reclamation in 1923—came to their rescue. The Bureau helped build Jackson Dam on the upper Snake River in Wyoming in 1907. The dam raised the level of Jackson Lake and provided some additional water, but it also added a new layer of complexity. The reservoir that was supposed to provide a long-term solution to relieve conflict seemed to do just the opposite.

Trouble began when the gates at Jackson Dam closed in early 1911. Though dam tenders still allowed the calculated natural stream flow through the gates, skeptical farmers downstream were sure the dam operators were depriving them of their water. By July the upper valley irrigators faced declining flows just when the lower valley irrigators began calling for their stored water. Though natural flows were declining in the upper river, the river still looked full. Upper valley irrigators looking at the full river couldn't believe that their share was dropping and that they faced cuts. The upstream irrigators always felt like they had plenty of water and didn't need any storage space in the reservoir. But now the tables had turned. The upper river farmers were going dry while they watched water running past their closed head gates to downstream users.

The Twin Falls Canal Company has a storage contract for 98,000 acre-feet of water in Jackson Lake, released from these Jackson Dam spillway gates.

The 1910 decree, though not released until August 1911, put upstream irrigators at ease and banked the fires of discontent. With their older priority rights now secure, they became more generous and willing to release water during dry years. Well established priorities allowed certainty and that encouraged cooperation. This spirit of cooperation helped reduce the inevitable conflicts, especially among junior users, when short water was not perfectly allocated in a constantly fluctuating natural river. But cooperation was short-lived.

In 1914, irrigators' head gates in the upper valley were being closed while stored water still flowed in the Snake River. Some irrigators were again convinced that government operators at

Jackson Dam were depriving them of their natural flow rights. Some thought officials miscalculated the natural flow. A compromise was worked out with the Reclamation Service, which resulted in another modification of Jackson Dam. In 1916, the dam was rebuilt, adding 400,000 acre-feet of storage. Some of that space would be allocated to upper valley irrigators.

For decades, irrigators paid twelve cents per acre-foot for water stored in Jackson Dam for nearly a century, but that was eventually raised to forty-one cents in 1990, when the dam was replaced. Because the old dam was unsafe, the federal government paid about 85 percent of the replacement cost. Most of its stored water would be sent downstream to the Twin Falls and Minidoka projects below Blackfoot. The Twin Falls Canal Company holds about 98,000 acre-feet of storage in the enlarged reservoir.

Jackson Lake reservoir stores 847,000 acre-feet of water, most of it for irrigation in south-central Idaho.

But moving stored water downstream added to the complexity of managing the system, and made allocation difficult. To get to the Twin Falls and Minidoka irrigators, the water from Jackson flowed right past Rigby and Blackfoot. An irrigator short of water, standing on the riverbank in Rigby, could not distinguish by looking at the river how much was natural flow and how much was stored water moving downstream. Water masters had to calculate the relative amounts of natural flow and stored water. Add to that the losses from seepage and evaporation from the reservoir and from the length of the river. To deliver ten thousand cubic feet per second at Milner Dam three hundred miles downstream from Jackson, the water master had to release considerably more than that.

The most junior rights, always the first to feel the effects, complained the most about accounting. It was understandably hard for water-short farmers in the upper valley to let water flow past their head gates. Most refused to accept the assurances that it was water stored in Jackson Lake for irrigators in the lower valley. Some just took what they needed. It was a recipe for distrust as upriver and downriver users struggled for control of the river. The conflict bred resentment and suspicion that smolders just below the surface today.

In those days, the water master responsible for the fair and equitable allocation of water from Wyoming to Milner Dam was John Empey. His was nearly an impossible job. But in 1917, he came up with an enduring solution to help end all the bickering. He suggested all irrigation organizations and government agencies meet in the spring to discuss the coming season to try to improve relations and coordinate the management of the river. From his suggestion grew perhaps the most powerful organization in all of southern Idaho.

Disagreements over water in the early twentieth century often led to conflict and occasionally violence — especially in drought years, when ditches didn't carry enough water to satisfy thirsty crops. Drought broke down cooperation, just as it dried and cracked the mud in empty ditches. Farmers argued over how much, whose turn and how long the water would run. The cooperation that had been essential to building dams and canal systems and allocating water efficiently existed mostly within individual districts and among canal company members. The habits of mutual assistance common among rural residents who shared objectives and built cooperative institutions did not spread among competing water users. Individual districts had managers, but there was no system of cooperation on the upper Snake River in its entirety from Jackson to Milner.

In April 1919, state engineer W.G. Swendsen took up Empey's suggestion. He picked nine men, three each from Henrys Fork, South Fork and the Minidoka-Twin Falls projects, who would provide the basis for an organization to handle water management from year to year on the river.

The cooperative resolution they worked out eventually became embodied in the Committee of Nine, officially founded in 1923 to operate and coordinate all parts of the complex system.

But 1919 turned out to be one of the driest years ever. As summer wore on, more junior rights were shut off. Chains and padlocks were not enough. Neighbors argued over the meager water supply. In one case, two farmers faced each other down at the locked head gate. Both were armed with irrigation shovels. The tension was too much. They came to blows, and one irrigator died.

The governor called out the National Guard to keep the peace. Some irrigators still were convinced the natural flow was being miscalculated. Some were convinced it was a scheme to take their water. Upper valley farmers claimed allocation practices favored stored water users in the lower valley, including the Twin Falls Canal Company. Water going over Shoshone Falls was taken as evidence that lower valley irrigators were squandering water while upper river farmers were going dry. The governor and state engineer defended the allocation methods, but calculating exactly the ratio of natural to stored water was virtually impossible. Any miscalculations were not the result of a conspiracy but the result of complex transmission and evaporation losses and gains from various springs and tributaries in the hundreds of miles of river. Any allocation system would be to some extent arbitrary. The solution had to be negotiated, to be acceptable to all.

Irrigators met in January 1923 to work out such a solution. More than sixty irrigation organizations appointed a committee to work out a cooperative plan for allocating water that year. Russell E. Sheppard of Jerome suggested two from the Henrys Fork area, four from the main and south fork of the Snake River and three from the Twin Falls, North Side and Minidoka projects. The committee took its name, the Committee of Nine, from that number. The group was developed as an advisory group to the state's Water District 1 on the upper Snake River to ensure the orderly delivery of water and to prevent future confusion over just how much of whose water was in the river. The committee now meets every year, usually in January at the airport in Pocatello, and usually well more than nine attend. It is a quasi-governmental committee with tremendous political power and can all but dictate water policy in southern Idaho. The group represents all the irrigation districts and canal companies in the Snake River valley and effectively controls water use in most of southern Idaho.

The group was so effective that in the 1950s, Idaho Governor Len Jordan asked members to help negotiate the use of Snake River waters with Wyoming, where much of the water in the river originated. Idaho secured 96 percent of it, and prevented Wyoming from using its 4 percent outside the Snake River Basin.

Powerful as it was, however, the Committee of Nine could not make it rain. In 1924, water again was short. Crops, especially on the north side of the Snake River, were threatened. Some farmers were ready to abandon their fields. Some were forced to haul water. On the Twin Falls tract, farmers who themselves suffered about $25 million in crop losses, shared water with the North Side. Russell Sheppard requested the Committee of Nine ask upper valley irrigators to let a little water go. With the improved relations among irrigators that had come with the committee, the farmers were willing to comply and the crops were saved. The compromise allowed natural flow rights holders to leave some water in the river in trade for water from reservoirs later in the season. Some of the natural flow was credited to stored water users. It was complex, and not without complaints, but the system seemed acceptable to all.

Water-short years, such as 1924, underscored the need for additional storage, some argued. Either that or retire some lands. The Committee of Nine convinced farmers that the natural flow most years had been overused by increased farmlands. Jackson and Minidoka Dams couldn't hold enough water to meet their needs. Only additional storage of winter and spring flows could increase the supply, especially for profitable late season crops such as beets and potatoes. It was becoming obvious to many that more land was being irrigated than the water supply could accommodate in dry years. And that helped convince holdouts of the need for additional storage.

The effort already was under way at American Falls. The dry summer of 1919 inspired a project, which began in 1921, to add storage on the river. The Idaho congressional delegation secured $1.7 million for the construction of the American Falls Dam. But before the dam could be built, the city of American Falls, with a population of about 1,100, had to be moved to higher ground. That alone cost about $3 million. (Even today, during low water years, sidewalks, curbs and building foundations like the ruins of a lost civilization can still be seen on the south side of the reservoir. When the reservoir is full, an old concrete grain silo rises like a monument to the former town submerged beneath the placid waters.) Idaho Power Company would have to move its power plant at the falls. Three miles of Union Pacific track would have to be relocated, and the Snake River bridge would have to be raised twenty-one feet. The project also required the cession of tribal lands. Interior Secretary Albert Fall quipped at the time, that the only irrigated farmland in the area would be inundated by the reservoir. And Idaho farmers already were delinquent on payments for the Minidoka project.

Idaho Governor David W. Davis, Senator William E. Borah, Russell Sheppard, the Committee of Nine and Idaho Power Company combined to form a formidable political force, all pushing for the project. Borah's persuasive influence convinced Fall, but only if the farmers would put up $250,000. A Reclamation Service lawyer suggested all the irrigation districts along the Snake River valley band together into a single unit to secure a loan. This was something new, and the idea met with typical southern Idaho farmer skepticism of federal government meddling. Large and small irrigation districts and canal companies would be combined into a single entity. The advantages were obvious—a single water district recognized by the state and the Reclamation Service would improve the financial strength of all the groups. But small irrigators feared they would be taken over by big districts. Some feared the idea would put newcomers in the lower valley on an equal footing with water users who had been in the area fifty years. Promoters reminded the skeptics of the lawsuits and hard feelings that came with water fights in dry years. The new project would increase the supply. They mailed out pamphlets and conducted public meetings. Support grew and many were simply swept up in the flood. In January 1924, the water users voted on the formation of the American Falls Irrigation District. A new level of cooperation emerged among irrigators, though not without some skeptics, with a vote of 7,228 to 1,254. And a district judge approved the results. The following May, a bond issue election garnered 93 percent of the votes to approve bonds worth $2.7 million. That was more than enough to pay the irrigators' share of the project and fulfill the deal Borah had cut with Fall. The irrigators eventually paid back the bonds. The state Supreme Court upheld the formation of the district.

The American Falls Dam, built by the newly renamed Bureau of Reclamation, was 5,227 feet long, eighty-three feet high, and seventy-five feet wide. The reservoir behind it was twenty-five miles long, and three and a half miles wide. It covered eighty-eight square miles, holding 1.7 million acre-feet. The dam itself cost $3.6 million. The whole project with the new town site and a new hydroelectric power plant added up to $8.5 million. The gates closed in October 1926, and the long reservoir began to fill. The reservoir reached capacity on July 1, 1927. It provided supplemental water for one million acres and enough water to irrigate an additional 115,000 acres north of the Minidoka Dam.

The other significant reservoir on the Snake River would be Palisades, on the Idaho-Wyoming border, authorized in 1941. But World War II delayed the construction of this reclamation project on the South Fork of the Snake River eight miles west of the border. The project was reauthorized in 1950. The Bureau of Reclamation completed the rock-faced earth-fill dam in 1959. The dam was 273 feet high, 2,200 feet long and forty feet wide at the top. The reservoir was twenty miles long, three miles wide and covered 16,100 acres. Today it holds 1.4 million acre-feet, and provides power production and flood control in addition to irrigation storage. The completed project cost about $76.6 million, of which irrigators paid about $11 million. Today it is one of the most important Snake River projects, supplying late season water to thousands of farmers on the North Side and Twin Falls tracts. Water users pay $9 per acre-foot to store water in the reservoir.

Over the years, American Falls, Palisades and other federal reservoirs on the upper Snake River have helped ensure water supplies that are overextended in most years, critically short in a few and, rarely, more than abundant. Except for the privately owned Milner Dam, the federal government built the reservoirs that made irrigation supplies more dependable. Farmers covered part of, but never the whole, cost of construction. Yet they display a proprietary attitude over water in the system built and operated by the federally funded Bureau of Reclamation. Irrigators wanted government services and were willing to put up with a little meddling in exchange for the Bureau to operate and maintain the dams and reservoirs of the Minidoka system. They traded away a measure of local control in return for the added dependability the federal reservoirs would bring. But they didn't like being told how to manage the water. Today the federal water managers in the Bureau's Burley office release water at the direction of the District 1 water master, who wields tremendous power, works for the Committee of Nine and also is paid by the Idaho Department of Water Resources. The water master is arguably one of the most powerful individuals in the state because of his influence on water policy and his control over the water in a substantial part of southern Idaho.

The number of reservoirs and their capacity has grown over the years. Today the system holds more than four million acre-feet—enough to irrigate one million acres. The reservoirs provide enough storage to capture the ample spring runoff from wet years and carry irrigators through a couple of dry years. As the dry years continue, however, the call for the federal government to build more reservoirs grows louder. But so far it has been tempered by the skepticism that resulted from the colossal failure of the Teton Dam on the morning of June 5, 1976. The ensuing flood killed eleven people, caused about $350 million in damages, and left thousands of acres flooded. The dam was designed to stretch the storage capacity into extended dry periods.

Though dams and reservoirs stretched the water supplies through dry years, they didn't guarantee any more water. But having the extra stored water made water fights more rare.

The Committee of Nine provided a way for competing irrigators to cooperate, to work out their disagreements and to share meager supplies in dry years. The federal government provided ample storage, in most years anyway, with more than four million acre-feet of reservoir space in the Bureau's Minidoka Project. But all of that was upstream of Milner Dam. The river was officially allowed to run dry at Milner, splitting the state hydrologically. That meant everything downstream of Milner Dam would be separate and distinct from the upper Snake River—theoretically. The Twin Falls Canal Company tract, however, sits right on the dividing line between those two regions, and thus is affected by what happens in both. The tract draws water from the region upstream of Milner, but runoff from the tract forms part of the flow in the river downstream of the dam. In the early 1980s, that flow would become central to a water fight that threatened to tear the state apart. The battle line was etched across the great lava plain of southern and eastern Idaho. East of this jagged line, water ran into the Snake above Milner; to the west, water ran into the river below Milner.

Henry Schodde's water wheels already had shown that seniority was not necessarily enough to protect a water right. By rights of seniority, his water wheels should have been allowed to run. But letting them run to irrigate one hundred sixty acres would have eliminated the construction of Milner Dam, preventing the development of irrigation systems that today provide water to nearly half a million acres. From that perspective, the judges of Schodde's day were right. They understood that the prior appropriation doctrine came with conditions. Their decision articulated a basic tenet in Idaho water law: Prior appropriation should not be used to block the fullest, most efficient development of the state's water resources. That concept became the focus of a landmark lawsuit filed some seventy years later, and it eventually would threaten the senior water right of the Twin Falls Canal Company. This fight was bigger than the Committee of Nine. The battles would be fought in courtrooms, in the State House and in Congress. It was the largest lawsuit in Idaho history, and it would affect water rights in thirty-eight of the state's forty-four counties.

The entire state was about to learn—those who hadn't already—that the first to develop a water right doesn't always prevail in the fight over water, especially when political might can bend the law. And it all started with one man and a new, powerful groundwater pump.

Courtesy Twin Falls Canal Co.

The railroad arrived in Twin Falls in August 1905.

Chapter Thirteen:
Showdown at Swan Falls

People thought Julian Clawson was crazy when he hauled a drilling rig out into the sagebrush on the Snake River Plain north of Rupert. Some thought he was drilling for oil. When he told them he was drilling for water, they were sure he was nuts. But Clawson, a Salt Lake City businessman, was anything but crazy. In 1946, he had bought several thousand acres of dry farmland at the edge of the Bureau of Reclamation's Minidoka Project north of the Snake River. At the time, most farmers irrigated their fields with gravity flows from surface diversions, some used pumps to lift water to higher canals and some pumped water from shallow aquifers. Clawson had no surface water, and his land was beyond the reach of gravity irrigation. In 1947, however, he found nine wells on his land abandoned thirty years earlier by German immigrants.

Clawson wasn't just lucky. He had studied 1928 geological reports that showed large amounts of groundwater beneath the arid lava plain. But it was deep, more than four hundred feet in some places. Clawson, undaunted, invested in the best high-lift pumps available at the time, and he drilled three deep, twenty-inch-diameter wells. The reports were right. He found lots of water— enough to irrigate thirty-eight hundred acres of wheat, potatoes and beans. After seventy days of continuous pumping, the aquifer showed no drop in the water table. Other farmers began to watch with interest. Maybe he wasn't really crazy after all.

Clawson could not have known the effects of groundwater development that followed his lead. It eventually would affect the relationship between the Eastern Snake River Plain Aquifer and the Twin Falls Canal Company's surface water right. It also would touch off the biggest water fight in Idaho history.

Within four years, Clawson was irrigating twenty-four thousand acres. Others followed, and soon they were irrigating another thirty thousand acres in the area with pumped groundwater. Bureau of Reclamation test wells confirmed the water supply. The new technology Clawson used made deep groundwater accessible. Many saw it as a new source of water that would spur agricultural development at a time when most water sources already were overallocated. The aquifer also was a source not directly affected by drought. It did not fluctuate with the cycle of dry and wet years.

Rain and snow that fell in the mountains in eastern Idaho as long ago as the Civil War had seeped into the ground and become part of the aquifer. That water is now, 150 years later, flowing out of the springs that line the north side of the Snake River. The water lies in the thin sediment deposits that separate successive layers of basalt laid down over eons. And it lies far below the surface, about six hundred feet at the upper end in eastern Idaho and less than two hundred feet where it flows out of the north wall of the Snake River Canyon in the ten-mile stretch of springs known as Thousand Springs, west of Twin Falls. The upper two hundred to five hundred feet of the aquifer hold up to four hundred million acre-feet. It is one of the most productive groundwater systems in the world, discharging eight to ten million acre-feet per year.

Around the time gravity-fed, surface irrigation began—before Milner Dam and the Twin Falls canal system were completed—farmers spread millions of acre feet of water on the lands in eastern Idaho. Part of that water seeped into the ground, affecting the level of the aquifer. Before the turn of the century, the aquifer discharged thirty-eight to forty-two hundred cubic feet per second at Thousand Springs. But with the irrigation water seeping into the ground, the flows at Thousand Springs began to increase. The springs peaked in the mid-1950s at sixty-eight hundred to seven thousand cubic feet per second.

The effects of Clawson's pumps alone could not be seen in the aquifer, but as the number of wells grew and as fewer farmers spread water on the ground, the effects slowly began to be seen in reduced discharge from the springs. More and more farmers began to augment their surface irrigation water with groundwater to take advantage of high crop prices, and many began irrigating new land with groundwater. In the early 1950s, nearly one million acres came into production. More farmers were pumping water from the aquifer and spreading less water on the ground. Surface irrigation diversions eventually decreased by about 800,000 acre-feet, while groundwater pumping grew unrestrained. The result began to show up at Thousand Springs and other springs along the river. The flows, which had been increasing, leveled off and began declining. By 1990 Thousand Springs had dropped to about 5,500 cubic feet—still more than historic levels, but a continued decline.

I.C. Russell, courtesy U.S.G.S.

Almost 5,000 cubic feet per second drop 180 feet from the layered basalt canyon walls at Thousand Springs in 1901.

Because Milner Dam dried up the Snake River during the irrigation season, any water in the river downstream of the dam came from spring flows fed by the aquifer. Runoff from fields and tributary streams also contributed to the river flow. The decline in the flows at Thousand Springs in the 1960s and 1970s, however, clearly showed the link between groundwater and surface water.

In 1948, about eighty deep well pumps were in use. By 1955, the number had jumped to 350 and climbing. This was one of the most significant postwar changes in Idaho agriculture. People drilled for water as though it were oil. Today one-third of the Eastern Snake River Plain is irrigated with groundwater from fifty-three hundred wells. Irrigation accounts for 95 percent of the groundwater use. But water users are pumping about 250,000 acre-feet more per year than flows back into the ground, and the aquifer level is dropping.

In addition, the improvements in pump technology in the 1960s allowed high-lift pumping directly from the river, such as at the Bell Rapids Project west of Twin Falls. Farmers inspired by high crop prices set up pumps powered by electricity from Idaho Power to lift water six hundred feet to the fertile bluffs above the famed Hagerman Fossil Beds National Monument. Up there, farmers paid $125 per acre in 2000, just for the electricity to bring the water to their fields.

State officials were slow to acknowledge the effects of the new pump technology on the aquifer and the Snake River. For decades they issued water rights to groundwater pumpers with little concern over who might be affected. Some were convinced there was so much water in the aquifer that pumping would not affect the water table. Over the years, however, the cumulative effect of groundwater development has affected some older surface water rights along the river. The Idaho Department of Water Resources, arguing that state law mandated full development of the resource, did little to protect those rights. Water Resources issued more permits. More wells were drilled. More water was pumped.

The move to groundwater development in southern Idaho changed the face of irrigation, and the unrestrained development of groundwater eventually threatened senior surface water rights, including that of the Twin Falls Canal Company. But the issue was much bigger. The growing demand for electric power and the decreasing spring flows touched off a bitterly fought battle that would change assumptions about basic Idaho water law and would reverberate across the state and beyond the dusty sagebrush plains to the halls of Congress.

Idaho Power Company, which supplied electricity to many of the new irrigation pumps, seemed to turn a blind eye to the connection between the increased pumping and diminishing flows from springs that fed the Snake River, which drove the company's hydroelectric plants. Perhaps there were good reasons, however. The company, a private utility and the major electric power producer in southern Idaho, was quick to see the potential market for power. The utility encouraged pumping and supplied the growing demand for power to drive the pumps. To meet the demand it had created, Idaho Power doubled its generating capacity in less than a decade. But even as the utility promoted the increased use of electricity to run irrigation pumps, its ability to generate that electricity with inexpensive hydropower began declining. In good water years, Idaho Power produces up to 60 percent of its electricity at seventeen hydroelectric plants on the Snake River. The rest is generated at coal-burning plants in Wyoming, Nevada and Oregon.

In the 1970s, Idaho Power's answer to the rising demands, however, was to propose a controversial coal-burning power plant in southern Idaho. Established agriculture interests and Republican lawmakers supported the proposal. But local voters and the Public Utilities Commission rejected the coal-fired plant because of environmental concerns and projected power rate increases.

The issue came to a head in 1977, the driest year on record in Idaho. John Peavey, erstwhile Republican state senator and sheep rancher from Ketchum, seized the issue. He clearly saw that increased groundwater pumping to irrigate new croplands was driving up the demand for power, while reducing the amount of water available to turn hydropower turbines. Meeting the increased demand with a new coal-burning plant would be expensive and would raise power rates to all but the irrigators: Idaho Power estimated that rates could double. The issue catapulted Peavey to prominence in southern Idaho politics. Idaho Power, however, fought back by funding a successful campaign to get Peavey out of office. Peavey returned to the Senate in the following election as a Democrat, also more in line with the increasingly Democratic stronghold in Ketchum and the Wood River Valley.

Idaho Power customers, lead by Peavey, filed a complaint with the Idaho Public Utilities Commission arguing that the company had failed to protect its water rights. The complaint sought a $200 million refund for ratepayers. "The company has a duty to its ratepayers to protect its property from waste, loss, damage or diversion from public service and to manage and operate its electrical plants in an efficient manner," Peavey wrote in the complaint signed by thirty-one other ratepayers. "The company has failed to meet its duty. It has lost some of its water rights. It stands ready to lose more."

The issue had started simply enough. To recap, power from the Bureau of Reclamation's Minidoka Dam ran Clawson's pumps. His pumps did not affect the Bureau's water supply. But many of the farmers who followed his lead ran their pumps with electricity from Idaho Power Company, and they pumped from the same aquifer that supplied the river downstream of Milner Dam. Idaho Power owned the right to a certain minimum amount of water in the river, which the company relied on to generate electricity. But protecting Idaho Power's minimum flow would affect further development of groundwater resources in the Eastern Snake River Plain Aquifer.

Less obvious was the connection between the Twin Falls Canal Company's 1900 surface water right based on springs at the upper end of the American Falls Reservoir. The springs flow at an average of 2,600 cubic feet per second, not enough to fill the canal company's right to 3,000 cubic feet. Yet new groundwater pumpers were allowed in the area that affected those springs. The springs decline noticeably during the irrigation season when groundwater pumps are going, forcing the canal company to rely increasingly on water stored in leased space in federal reservoirs. The issue is the same as with Idaho Power. New groundwater pumping diminished senior surface water rights, but upholding the senior rights would affect development.

Both cases presented real dilemmas. State water managers saw groundwater pumping as a way to develop the vast resources of the Eastern Snake River Plain Aquifer. But protecting Idaho Power's and the Twin Falls Canal Company's senior water rights meant curtailing or outright shutting down new groundwater pumpers. And that put a stick in the spokes of economic development. The case at hand grew directly from putting economics and resource development ahead of the prior appropriation doctrine.

The case would focus on Idaho Power's water right at a humble run-of-the-river hydroelectric plant at Swan Falls, in the narrow basalt canyon of the Snake River south of Boise. Here, in 1901, the Trade Dollar Mining Company had built the first hydropower dam on the Snake River. The nine-hundred-kilowatt facility was intended to supply power to the mines and the town of Silver City in the Owyhee Mountains twenty-eight miles to the south. Idaho Power bought the plant and its associated water rights in 1915. Over the years, the company rebuilt the plant and increased its capacity. In November 1982, even as the issue over Idaho Power's water rights raged, the Federal Energy Regulatory Commission renewed the utility's license and permitted it to renovate the Swan Falls facility and expand its capacity to twenty-five megawatts.

Swan Falls Dam straddles the Snake River south of Boise.

The company's water rights at Swan Falls total 9,450 cubic feet per second. Three rights with a priority date of 1900, total 5,450 cubic feet per second. A fourth added 4,000 cubic feet in 1919. But the company's recognized water right was limited by the plant capacity. The original plant turbines had a capacity of only 3,300 cubic feet per second, the rest ran unused past the powerhouse. The rebuilt plant had an increased capacity of 8,400 cubic feet.

Some argued, not unjustifiably, that there's rarely that much water in the river.

About five miles downstream from Swan Falls, at the town of Murphy, a U.S. Geological Survey gauging station has supplied continuous flow records since 1902. The gauge records showed average flow past Swan Falls was 6,800 cubic feet per second in winter and more than 4,500 in summer. The lowest flow on record was 4,530 cubic feet in the summer of 1981.

Peavey's complaint forced Idaho Power to stand up for its water rights. To defend itself, Idaho Power filed a lawsuit in state district court in 1978 against water users, claiming the company's water rights were senior to their irrigation water rights. The water users argued that Idaho Power had abandoned a portion of its original water right through lack of use and by encouraging electricity-dependent groundwater pumpers to develop more ground. They argued the company should not be allowed to assert its seniority. The district court sided with the water users, ruling that Idaho Power's older hydropower water right was subordinate to the later irrigation rights—that is water rights for irrigation held a preference over water rights for hydroelectric power generation.

Idaho Power, however, appealed the ruling to the state Supreme Court, which in 1982, reversed the district court decision in part. The Supreme Court ruled that the company's 8,400 cubic feet per second at Swan Falls Dam was senior to the irrigators and not subordinate to irrigation rights. The Court sent the case back to the district court, however, to determine whether Idaho Power may have forfeited part of that water right by not opposing diversions that depleted the flow at Swan Falls.

The Supreme Court ruling shook the water user establishment and state government to its foundations. The ruling, the most significant in Idaho water law, marked a turning point in state history. It's unintended effect put Idaho Power in control of water use and development in southern and eastern Idaho. The Court had stirred up a hornet's nest.

Lawmakers and state officials sided with the junior water right holders, in apparent conflict with the state's basic principle of prior appropriation. Despite the doctrine that granted preference to older water rights, the Idaho Legislature and the state's largely Republican leadership wanted to strip Idaho Power's water right of its seniority. They contended that the river and any further development on the Eastern Snake River Plain were far too important to be in the control of a private company.

The catch was clear. Since the state Supreme Court already had ruled on the issue, subordinating Idaho Power's right would require legislative action. Yet the state considers a water right a property right that can't be diminished without compensation. The underlying issue was which water right should be given priority in the Snake River Basin. Should it be for power production or should irrigation and industrial development be first in line? And who should decide? The issues pitted ratepayers against Idaho Power, ratepayers and Idaho Power against some irrigators, and some irrigators against other irrigators.

State Senator Laird Noh, a Twin Falls Republican, sheep rancher and chairman of the Senate Environment and Natural Resources Committee, emerged as the leader of those who favored subordinating the power company's water right. Noh argued that Idaho Power was not entitled to its entire water right, in spite of its seniority. The Supreme Court's ruling essentially made Idaho Power the state's water master, Noh said. "If a person wants to expand his farm, or divert through a trout farm, he's going to have to go to Idaho Power for permission, not the state," he said. The state's control of the Snake River could only be maintained by subordinating Idaho Power's rights, he argued.

Thoughtful and articulate, Noh was well regarded in his home district. He was an astute supporter of Twin Falls area interests. He understood well the implications of the Swan Falls case on the Twin Falls Canal Company's efforts to protect its own water rights from increased groundwater development, an issue that would resurface years after the Swan Falls case was settled.

But Idaho Power, objecting to any legislation that would subordinate its water right, proposed a compromise. It would give up part of its water right, in exchange for compensation and protection against legal challenges from ratepayers. Idaho Power would give up as much of its water right as necessary to protect existing water users if the Legislature would protect the company from future lawsuits and take away the Public Utilities Commission's control of the company's water rights.

Senator Noh introduced legislation in the Senate that embodied the compromise. But the bill lost by a single vote in the Senate, which instead approved a one-year, $35,000 study to determine whether subordination was necessary to maintain state control of the Snake River; to calculate any compensation to Idaho Power for subordinated water rights; and to examine the relationship between the river and the aquifer. Especially important was the relationship between the aquifer and the stream flows. This relationship was the underlying issue of the Swan Falls case and continues to be the issue facing the Twin Falls Canal Company and junior groundwater users upstream.

In May 1983, Idaho Power filed another lawsuit, naming 7,500 water users, in an effort to make a show of protecting its water rights. Idaho Power was in trouble with the Public Utilities Commission precisely because the company had failed to protect its water right at Swan Falls. Skeptics said this second lawsuit merely gave the company additional leverage over the backs of the irrigators.

Meanwhile, the Idaho Water Resources Board proposed the state simply buy the Swan Falls Dam and its water rights. Board chairman and Castleford farmer Don Kramer asked the state Department of Water Resources to study the proposal. But Idaho Power didn't think much of the idea. The company vowed to fight any attempt to take over the Swan Falls facility — to the U.S. Supreme Court if necessary.

Some suggested the market should decide the issue.

A University of Idaho study predicted the condemnation of the water right at Swan Falls would amount to a loss of $14.2 million in potential annual revenue and result in 12 percent to 14 percent rate increases to customers. That same water would open about 195,000 acres for agriculture, contributing $45 million to the state's economy. But that new production also would add to crop surpluses and help depress crop prices.

Despite all that maneuvering in 1983, the only bill to get through the Legislature was one authorizing the governor and attorney general to negotiate a settlement with Idaho Power and establishing committees to study various aspects of the issue.

Neither side let up.

In July 1983, Idaho Power and the Department of Water Resources proposed an agreement that would protect 5,000 of the 7,500 water users named in the company's lawsuit. In return, the state would protect Idaho Power from complaints from ratepayers over sacrificing low-cost hydropower rates. Only those who started using water after the 1982 court decision would still be included in the lawsuit. However, Governor John Evans, a Democrat from Malad, refused to sign the agreement.

When Idaho Power in January 1984 proposed a bill that would essentially adopt the proposed agreement, Idaho Attorney General Jim Jones, a Republican, characterized the legislation as a sinister effort to establish an unrestricted stranglehold on the Snake River. The issue was not between ratepayers and irrigators, he said, but between Idaho Power and the people of Idaho over control of the river.

Many who favored subordination tried to cast Idaho Power as a faceless, heartless corporation, victimizing the struggling family farmer. Though Idaho Power perhaps deserved to lose part of its water right, the company did not instigate the fight. Only after ratepayers brought their complaint against the utility did Idaho Power file its lawsuit against the water users. Even the state Senate acknowledged that water managers did not know whether Idaho Power's water right would give the company the control that Jones feared. Idaho Power was not the only large water user on the river. And any future development in eastern Idaho was far more likely to be driven by economic conditions, not just the availability of water.

The truth was that no one really knew just how much water already was appropriated and how much was available for any development. The problem was one of allocation, not control. Essentially the state was trying to blame Idaho Power for its own failings. State officials had allowed water in the Snake River Basin to be over-appropriated. The problem was not bullying by a private corporation; the company and the state shared the blame. The company had promoted increased pumping and failed to protect its own water rights. The state had failed to develop and keep accurate records of existing water rights, without which the prior appropriation doctrine simply can't work. The state also promoted groundwater development and issued permits under the guise of full economic development of the resource, allowing groundwater to be withdrawn at a greater rate than it could be recharged. Officials allowed development with only partial knowledge of who had what rights for how much water and who might be affected. And in reality, irrigators had far more control of the river than they accused Idaho Power of trying to gain.

Support for stripping the seniority from Idaho Power's water right, however, was far from unanimous in the Legislature. Some lawmakers questioned the constitutionality of subordination. "This is getting us away from the concept of first in time, first in right. If we pass this nobody's water right is sacred," Rep. Gordon Hollifield of Jerome told the Twin Falls *Times-News*. House Speaker Tom Stivers of Twin Falls—who opposed the subordination of water rights—assigned Idaho Power's bill to the State Affairs Committee. Stivers, along with conservationists, said flows should be maintained in the river to preserve abundant low cost hydropower, as well as what was left of native fish habitat. More farmland was not needed. He also argued that water rights were property rights, and the loss of a water right at Swan Falls was a loss of private property.

Both sides had incentive to negotiate an agreement. If legislation failed, the issue would be settled in court. And the memory of the Supreme Court's ruling remained fresh. While the two sides continued to negotiate, the fight raged on in the Senate, pitting Noh against Peavey. Noh favored stripping Idaho Power's water right of its seniority; Peavey held that the utility had failed to protect its water right on behalf of its ratepayers. Yet by defending the rights of ratepayers, Peavey had now taken Idaho Power's side. In February 1984, the Senate killed subordination a second time—this time by two votes. But Noh in turn was able to block Peavey's proposals requiring compensation for the utility's lost water rights.

Finally, in October 1984, the state and Idaho Power reached an agreement. Idaho Power abandoned its claim to 8,400 cubic feet per second at Swan Falls in exchange for a state mandated minimum flow of 3,900 cubic feet during the irrigation season and 5,600 cubic feet in the winter. The lowest flow on record at Swan Falls had been just over 4,500 cubic feet during the irrigation season. That left six hundred cubic feet for future upstream development—at no more than twenty thousand acres per year—to maintain a minimum flow of 3,900 cubic feet at Swan Falls. Six hundred cubic feet per second, at eighty acres per cubic foot on average, would irrigate forty-eight thousand acres. Idaho Power dropped five thousand water users from its lawsuit—keeping only those who had filed after the Supreme Court ruling—in exchange for a promise that it would not be penalized for failing to protect its water right.

The Legislature approved the Swan Falls Agreement in February 1985, settling Idaho Power's two district court lawsuits. It sought to bring balance among competing demands for a limited resource—a public policy issue perhaps best resolved outside the courtroom. Probably most important, the agreement also called for a general water right adjudication of the entire Snake River Basin, which would establish accurate records for more than 150,000 water rights in thirty-eight of the state's forty-four counties.

Critics said Idaho Power gave away too much. Jim Jones claimed the agreement put the state back in control of the river and future development. Some accused the state of placing the needs of irrigators and other water users above the hydropower generation needs of Idaho Power and its customers. Idaho conservationists raised concerns that the agreement would have substantial effects on fish and wildlife in the river. Water Resources Director Keith Higginson called the case the end of unfettered water development in Idaho.

But the fight was far from over.

Later in 1985, in a move that threatened to unravel the pact, the U.S. Fish and Wildlife Service and the National Marine Fisheries Service, the Natural Resources Legal Defense Foundation and the Idaho Wildlife Federation raised significant concerns about the effects the proposed minimum flows in the Snake River might have on fish and wildlife, including diminishing salmon and steelhead runs in the Snake, Salmon and Clearwater rivers. The Fish and Wildlife Service asked the Federal Energy Regulatory Commission to deny Idaho Power's petition to reset flows as established in the agreement. Because the Commission—known as FERC—administered licenses for private hydro projects, it also had to approve the agreement.

Lowering minimum flows at Swan Falls would expose up to half the islands that make up the Deer Flat National Wildlife Refuge to predators and leave them vulnerable to human disturbance by linking them to the mainland during low flows. The refuge, established in 1937 to protect nesting migratory birds, now comprises 94 islands in the Snake River from Swan Falls to Farewell Bend. Fish and Wildlife claimed a water right—though not quantified—greater than 5,600 cubic feet per second to protect the islands. But the agency had never asserted its water right, relying instead on Idaho Power's right, which provided enough water. A Fish and Wildlife official said the state hadn't considered federal lands when it negotiated the Swan Falls Agreement. No one had talked about the fish and wildlife that depended on the river.

In October 1986, Congress weighed in when U.S. Senator James McClure, an Idaho Republican, tried to force FERC to act on the agreement. FERC had received a copy of the agreement in October 1984, but had not yet ruled on it.

The Fisheries Service—now known as NOAA Fisheries—and Fish and Wildlife agreed to withdraw their concerns with the understanding they could raise them during the state's water rights adjudication, a move they would come to regret.

Idaho conservation groups argued that FERC must prepare an environmental impact statement before approving the agreement. They also argued that the commission should not approve any flow lower than that necessary to protect Fish and Wildlife's reserved right for enough water to maintain the Deer Flat islands. The 3,900 cubic feet per second minimum set by the agreement was based on politics, not on any biologically adequate flow. And the commission was obligated under federal law to protect, mitigate and enhance wildlife at the refuge, the groups said.

Still FERC did not act.

In a 1987 letter to House committee head John D. Dingell,

FERC Chairwoman Martha O. Hesse said the commission had not acted on the issue because it didn't know whether an environmental impact statement was required; whether an implied federal water right existed for the Deer Flat refuge; whether the settlement satisfied the Northwest Power Planning Council's Fish and Wildlife Program; and whether the settlement complied with the Federal Power Act.

Further complicating things, on September 2, 1987, the Confederated Tribes of the Umatilla Reservation and Columbia River Inter-Tribal Fish Commission raised concerns about the effect of flows that already were too low during salmon and steelhead migration. And then, just as legislation introduced by an Idaho Democrat, U.S. Representative Richard Stallings, was under consideration in the House Energy and Commerce Committee, the state of Washington wanted to know what effect the agreement would have on the rest of the Pacific Northwest. In December 1987, Congress ultimately passed the bill, and President Reagan signed it. It gave the U.S. Fish and Wildlife Service, the National Marine Fisheries Service and Idaho Power $2.65 million to study the effects of minimum flows. But it did not require FERC to act on the study's findings.

In August 1989, Fifth District Judge Dan Hurlbutt dismissed the lawsuits that were at the basis of the Swan Falls dispute. He also was hearing the Snake River Basin Adjudication, mandated by the agreement. It had been assigned to Hurlbutt's Fifth District Court in Twin Falls because the court was roughly the geographic center of the case. It would be an accounting of about 150,000 water rights in the Snake River Basin. The case was so big, a courthouse was built to hold offices for judge and staff and records.

The Swan Falls case may have been resolved out of court, but the underlying issues continued to smolder. The question of how groundwater development affects surface water flows in the Snake River was far from settled. In 1988 the North Side and Twin Falls canal companies sought a halt to upstream development. The companies charged that new wells were reducing the springs that flow into American Falls Reservoir, which supplied much of the companies' water rights. State water officials recognized that development in the upper basin affected flows below Milner Dam. But studies showed the effects of small diversions in the upper basin could not be determined, and the full effects of any diversion might not be evident for many years.

In 1992, the Twin Falls and North Side canal companies filed a lawsuit against the Idaho Department of Water Resources to halt development on the Snake River Plain. Their complaint was essentially a replay of the Swan Falls issue. It reopened the long-festering resentment between upriver and downstream water users. The companies opposed seven hundred pending groundwater permit applications. Water Resources agreed to hold the applications until the matter was settled. The action by the two canal companies was soon overshadowed by a more important case that eventually forced the state to not only acknowledge the connection between ground and surface water, but actually begin to manage the two sources together—a concept known as conjunctive management.

The next major battle began with a simple call for a few cubic feet of water from a spring north west of Twin Falls. The fundamental issue in this case—as in the Swan Falls case—was understanding the interaction between ground and surface water and managing the cumulative effects of junior groundwater rights on senior surface water rights.

It was no longer just a question of who came first.

Bisbee photo No. 172, Courtesy Twin Falls Public Library
Grubbing sagebrush with a team of horses on the Twin Falls tract.

Chapter Fourteen:
Mining the Aquifer

The first sign of trouble came as 1991 turned to 1992 and the winter snows in the mountains of western Wyoming fell far short of expectations. As winter edged toward spring, the mountain snowpack that normally provides the summer's water supply in the Snake River Basin was at a record low. Following on a string of dry years, the meager snowpack and earlier than usual runoff brought on by warmer than usual weather set the stage for what would be one of the driest years on record in southern Idaho. That year, water would not be available for many water rights that ordinarily are fully filled. The Twin Falls Canal Company would be forced to cut its delivery to farmers by one-third for the first time since American Falls Dam was completed in 1927. State officials faced the unpopular move of shutting off 470 water users below Milner Dam whose rights were junior to a 1976 agreement for a minimum stream in the Snake River at the U.S. Geological Survey gauge at Weiser, west of Boise, where the river meets Oregon. Wells ran dry and spring flows dwindled, including those that supplied the Twin Falls Canal Company's water right.

"Things are about to come unglued in southern Idaho," predicted Sherl Chapman, then executive director of the Idaho Water Users Association.

On May 15, 1992, the Idaho Department of Water Resources issued a moratorium on all new or pending applications for ground and surface water rights in the southern two-thirds of the state. It would remain in effect as long as necessary, as long as the drought persisted. A howl went up from some who needed water, but most irrigators recognized the moratorium as an overdue response to intensifying water supply issues. A growing number of groundwater pumpers, the decreasing amount of flood irrigation on the Snake River Plain, and reduced recharge from a string of dry years had dropped the level of the huge Eastern Snake River Plain Aquifer. "Lowered ground water levels also reduce spring discharge needed to maintain stream and river flows," R. Keith Higginson, director of the Idaho Department of Water Resources, wrote in the moratorium order. Those reduced discharges included the springs at the upper end of the American Falls Reservoir. And those springs make up a substantial portion of the Twin Falls Canal Company's water right of three thousand cubic feet per second at Milner Dam.

The moratorium was a direct response to pressure from the canal company and other water users who complained that continued development of surface and groundwater had affected existing uses and supplies. A lot of irrigators and fish farmers who rely on spring flows were worried. The North Side Canal Company depends largely on stored water in the American Falls Reservoir and a small amount of natural flow in the Snake River. In recent years, the flow from the springs have dwindled as the irrigation season progressed. The canal companies blame increased groundwater pumping for the decrease, not just drought. What the river doesn't supply, the companies make up with stored water. They had pushed for some control on groundwater development on the upper Snake River Plain for at least seven years.

The dropping spring flows also threatened southern Idaho's thriving commercial trout industry in the Snake River Canyon. Set at the foot of Thousand Springs on the north side of the river west of Twin Falls, springs filled the raceways where Clear Springs Foods trout hatchery of Buhl raised an average of twenty million pounds of rainbow trout each year. The flows are vital to Clear Springs and other local trout producers that line the canyon. They depend on clean water at a nearly constant, cool 58 degrees year-round. If these springs dried up, the fish hatcheries would not be able to replace the lost water.

The Committee of Nine, the Upper Snake water advisory board, took no stand on the moratorium. It couldn't. The committee included irrigators who wanted permits to drill new wells as well as irrigators whose water rights were affected by groundwater pumping. But when domestic and irrigation wells were going dry and springs flows were dropping, it was hard for the committee to rationalize bringing new land under irrigation. Ron Carlson, water master of Water District 1, already had turned off the irrigation water to thirty-five farmers on the upper Snake River in eastern Idaho. "It doesn't make sense to continue pumping until the aquifer is understood better," Committee of Nine Chairman DeWitt Moss said.

But the moratorium wasn't enough for the canal companies. On July 24, 1992, they filed a formal complaint asking the district court for an injunction to prevent Water Resources from approving about 730 outstanding applications and pending permits for the diversion of more than 1,300 cubic feet per second of water to irrigate nearly 100,000 acres east of Milner Dam. The canal companies argued those permits would affect their senior surface water rights. They asked the court to block any action that would affect their water rights.

But Higginson was not ready to concede that groundwater pumpers were the problem. It's a big aquifer, and it's not likely to go dry, he maintained. Conservative estimates say it contains about two hundred million to four hundred million acre feet of water. About seven to eight million acre feet flow through the system each year. Current uses may be "just skimming the surface," Higginson said. Just how increased groundwater use affected other water rights remained unproven. To find out the extent of those effects, the state needed more information, but Higginson's department didn't have the money for the kind of study to answer such questions, he said.

Still, it seems clear today that the drive for economic development blinded some water managers to the potential consequences of continued growth of groundwater use.

Higginson had been appointed to head the Idaho Department of Water Resources in 1965. He graduated from the University of Utah in 1957 with a degree in civil engineering, and spent the first few years of his career with the Utah state engineer's office. He left his post in Idaho to serve as Commissioner of Reclamation under President Carter from 1977 to 1981. In 1987, Idaho Governor Cecil Andrus, a Democrat, re-appointed Higginson director of Water Resources, where he served until 1995. Though he was out of office during the thick of the Swan Falls battle, Higginson admitted he knew the two sources were connected. The Swan Falls case had proved that connection physically, legally and legislatively. But efforts to develop rules to manage the two sources together—a concept known in hydrologic circles as conjunctive management—was opposed by groundwater pumpers who continued to maintain the state had no way to show which pumpers were affecting the senior rights.

Courtesy Idaho Department of Water Resources

Increased groundwater use for sprinkler irrigation has affected other water rights.

The effects, however, were obvious. Regardless of how much water the aquifer held, pumping the groundwater lowered the level, and that affected spring flows, just like opening the drain lowers an overflowing bathtub. Higginson had made that point in his May 1992 moratorium.

The junior water pumpers defended themselves by arguing that the senior water users could not say which wells should be shut down. And they were right. It was not possible to point to a single well and say that well was affecting the Twin Falls right. But they overlooked one important point. Idaho water law puts the burden on the junior users, when challenged, to show that their pumping will not harm other, senior rights. That too was impossible. What was possible, however, was to say that wells within an area known to be tributary to the river would affect the springs, with the effect perhaps varying with distance.

The Twin Falls Canal Company complained that the state's approval of unrestrained groundwater development had forced it to defend itself against junior water rights. And again state officials, as they had in the Swan Falls case, turned their backs on the prior appropriation doctrine. When junior water rights affect senior rights, the canal company argued, development should halt, the pumps should be shut off, or some form of compensation be worked out. Water managers, who knew the effects of groundwater pumping on surface water rights, had allowed development although they could not pinpoint where the effects were likely to show up—and then used that as an excuse for inaction.

The state defended itself by saying it had no way of knowing which wells must be shut off to ensure the canal company's right—the pumpers' tired argument. And officials were not even sure that shutting off water rights would restore the spring flows or senior rights. The moratorium was at least recognition of the problem, even if officials couldn't agree on the exact cause or on a fair solution. And the moratorium gave the state an opportunity to build on some of what it had learned in the Swan Falls case. Officials and hydrologists had determined the area where the groundwater was tributary to the Snake River below Milner Dam with some confidence. They called it the "trust water" region in the 1984 Swan Falls Agreement—it was the six hundred cubic feet per second freed by the minimum flow and held in trust for future development. And from that they could easily say groundwater above that demarcation line would be tributary to the Snake River above Milner Dam. They listed this as the "nontrust water" region. But they were reluctant to delineate more specifically the area tributary to the springs in the upper end of American Falls

Reservoir. Some suggested the boundary between the two areas was the place to start. But the pumpers insisted those areas were too vague and too broad. Shutting off junior pumpers within the nontrust water area made no sense if doing so would not restore the senior rights. And it was not fair to halt all development just to satisfy a few senior rights.

The case appeared to be at a stalemate.

The landmark Swan Falls case had plainly shown that increased use of groundwater resulted in a measurable reduction in Idaho Power's senior water right. But Idaho Power, incredibly, still encouraged groundwater pumping by subsidizing rates. The utility was selling electric power to irrigation pumpers at less than the cost to supply that power. The subsidy dates to a general rate increase in the early 1970s, when Idaho Power agreed not to raise rates to groundwater pumpers if the pumpers would agree to pay their estimated bill at the beginning of the season. The estimated $13 million subsidy in electric rates to pumpers was later cut back to $11 million, but the cheap rates continued to encourage groundwater development. The subsidy increased groundwater use, lowered the aquifer level and in the bargain increased the amount of lift needed to bring it to the surface. In 1992, pumpers still paid their bills in advance at the subsidized rate.

As the 1992 irrigation season got under way, the clouds of a water war were building like a summer thunder storm over southern Idaho. Simmering discord between upper valley groundwater pumpers and lower valley irrigators threatened to spark renewed conflict. "Idaho's always had a water war of one sort or another," said state Senator Laird Noh of Twin Falls, who had led the fight against Idaho Power Company's senior water right in the Swan Falls case. He was now on the other side, defending the local canal company's senior right against junior groundwater pumpers.

An old Mark Twain quote, often repeated in the arid West, especially during dry years, was dusted off: "Whiskey is for drinking, and water is for fighting over." This fight would pit people who had water and would like to hang on to it, against those who wanted some water and were trying to elbow their way to the front of the line. In the sense that groundwater diversions already had affected senior water rights, the moratorium was very late in coming, Noh said. Idaho water law allows the senior water right holder to sue other users who may be affecting their right. But it was hard to believe—let alone for a senior water user to prove—that a new irrigation well in St. Anthony would affect water rights in Twin Falls about 150 miles to the southwest. The problems facing water users were a long-running lack of effective enforcement of water rights law and a lack of understanding of the interaction between surface and groundwater sources. Noh raised additional questions. How much of the current problem was related to drought and how much was related to human activity? When the drought ended would spring flows and senior water rights recover?

"The fact remains that water is a finite resource," Noh said. So far, no other states had successfully dealt with the dilemma of managing groundwater and surface water without causing economic losses for some users. The issue came to a head with a lawsuit filed in 1993 by a single water user on the north side of the river in the Hagerman Valley. The Twin Falls Canal Company watched with intense interest from the bench, for the outcome would affect its own water right.

For three years in the early 1990s, low water had forced Howard "Butch" Morris to cut back his acreage and change his cropping patterns, cutting into his earnings. Morris leased and farmed 480 acres in the Hagerman Valley northwest of Twin Falls. He also leased the right to 4.8 cubic feet per second of water from a spring that flowed out of the Martin-Curran Tunnel, with a priority date of April 1, 1892. Water in the spring came from the Eastern Snake River Plain Aquifer.

In 1991, low water forced Morris to set aside fifty acres. In 1992, he changed to crops that required less water. In 1993, he left idle a total of 100 acres. All this occurred because he couldn't get the water he was entitled to by the senior water right. Morris complained to his landlords, brothers Alvin and Tim Musser. On June 16, 1993, Morris and the Mussers made a formal request to the local water master for the "full and immediate delivery of their decreed water rights from the Curran Tunnel."

They weren't the first to complain about not getting their water from the Curran Tunnel. In May 1993, other irrigators with water rights from the same spring asked watermaster George Lemmon to deliver their full amount of water. Lemmon relayed the request to Department of Water Resources Director Keith Higginson, who rejected the request. Higginson denied Morris' request as well, saying he did not have the authority to tell Lemmon to "conjunctively administer ground and surface water within (the water district) short of a formal hydrologic determination that such conjunctive management is appropriate."

Morris and the Mussers took their case to the Fifth District Court in Twin Falls to force the director to deliver their water. The lawsuit also asked the court to force the director to administer water from the aquifer according to the state's prior appropriation doctrine. They asserted that state law did in fact give Higginson the authority to deliver their water. They argued that being outside a water district did not release him from that duty, as Higginson had argued. State law specifically authorizes the director to administer water rights that are outside an established water district. Within such districts, water rights are administered by a watermaster, such as Lemmon.

Water Resources moved to dismiss the case as moot because after the lawsuit was filed, the director had issued a notice of intent to establish rules for managing the aquifer and surface water together. Higginson also posted notice of a contested case, which would provide a forum for determining how to provide the Mussers' water, pending the completion of the rules. More red tape, but still no water. Higginson contended that without such rules, the department had no way to know what water rights should be shut off to increase the flow in the Curran Tunnel. He also noted that state law required the "complete economic utilization of the Snake River Aquifer." He was trapped between two tenets of the law. He knew he was responsible to distribute water rights based on priority when a demand or "call" for water was made to him. But he defended his refusal in court by arguing that without a legal finding setting out the connection between surface and groundwater in the area, groundwater rights could not be distributed through a water district.

His defense did not hold water.

Fifth District Judge Daniel Hurlbutt ruled that surface and groundwater in the Snake River Basin are generally interconnected and must, as a consequence, be administered conjunctively. He based the ruling on Higginson's own statements in a separate district court case. Higginson's department had submitted a previous report that noted the hydrologic connection between the Snake River Plain Aquifer and the springs tributary to the Snake River or other surface tributaries. During the trial, Higginson testified that throughout his nineteen-year tenure he had known that ground and surface water in the Snake River Basin were interconnected and must be managed conjunctively. Yet he had failed to develop the rules needed to manage the two sources together, Hurlbutt noted.

The trial court sided with Morris and the Mussers, ruling that it clearly was the director's job to distribute water under the prior appropriation doctrine, whether within a water district or not. Hurlbutt ruled that Higginson's failure to develop rules to manage ground and surface water together was not an excuse for failing to uphold the priority of the Mussers' water right. The absence of conjunctive management rules that would enable him to respond to the Mussers' demand for water was breach of his duty and not a valid reason for not providing the water to the Mussers. Hurlbutt ordered Higginson to provide the water under the prior appropriation doctrine as set out in the state Constitution. The state appealed the ruling, but the Idaho Supreme Court in 1994 upheld the district court ruling. The Court ruled that the director of the Department of Water Resources must obey state law and deliver the water necessary to fulfill the Musser's senior water right.

Ten years after the historic Swan Falls Agreement seemed to have settled the conflict between groundwater and surface water users, the Musser case forced the Department of Water Resources to develop rules to manage ground and surface water together — "conjunctive management" rules that would recognize the complex relationship between the Snake River and the Eastern Snake River Plain Aquifer. The rules also would recognize the seniority of surface water rights without shutting off junior water rights needlessly. And the rules eventually would help protect the Twin

Falls Canal Company's senior water right. But that didn't happen without some additional legal battles.

With a freshly minted law degree in hand, John Rosholt arrived in Twin Falls in 1964 to take up the practice of law. He began taking on divorce cases, but soon turned to more lucrative work settling water fights. Rosholt was born in Lewiston in 1937, proud of his Norwegian heritage. He earned a bachelor's degree from the University of Idaho in 1959 and his law degree in 1964. He soon went to work for a prestigious Twin Falls law firm, and over the years earned a reputation as one of the state's best water lawyers. He didn't have a lot of patience with environmentalists, but he knew the law, and he knew how to pick his fights and how to use the law to protect the irrigators he represented.

Rosholt deftly steered the canal company through the minefield of the Swan Falls case and many smaller cases before that. He and the Twin Falls Canal Company watched the Musser case closely. But he advised the canal company to back off and see what the state would do as a result of the case. After the case was settled, the state could no longer plead innocence. Officials promised to earnestly seek to craft some effective rules to manage ground and surface water sources. The state already had begun to take stock of who held what water right and to develop a map of the groundwater beneath the vast Eastern Snake River Plain—the country's most productive aquifer.

All water in the state belongs to the people of the state, and the state allocates water use on their behalf. But officials over the years allowed more water to be pumped from the aquifer than flows into it. That is known as groundwater mining, and it's against Idaho water law. Higginson, with some justification, defended the department, citing 1951 state legislation that called for the full development of the resource. That position, however, was what touched off the conflict between constitutionally protected senior water rights and what others considered the most productive use of water within the state. In the Musser case, as in the massive Swan Falls case, full development and prior appropriation collided head on. This time, Higginson was one of the courtroom casualties. Groundwater pumpers had changed the water level and the dynamics within the Snake River Plain Aquifer; established water rights were going dry, while on the plain, irrigators with newly drilled wells were pumping their full capacity.

The state's effort to develop rules to manage the two water sources together was a public process and about as painless as a root canal. Some advocated simply going back to a strict prior appropriation distribution. If senior rights aren't getting their water, all others must be shut off until they do. But managing the two water sources conjunctively isn't really that simple. It raises a number of complex questions.

What is the relationship between ground and surface waters? How should the prior appropriation doctrine, developed for surface water distribution, be applied to interconnected ground and surface waters? If shutting off junior wells has no immediate effect on senior surface rights, does it make sense to shut them off? Might some wells be hydrologically isolated by unseen underground features from nearby senior surface water sources? Legally, would conjunctive management treat water rights as if they come from the same source even when one is from groundwater and the other from surface water? Should junior water rights be protected just because they are pumped from a well?

Rosholt maintains that the prior appropriation doctrine is not subordinated to conjunctive management. The state Supreme Court already had ruled that Water Resources was obligated to administer the two sources together. Because of the complexity, conjunctive management carries a broader connotation than just managing the two together, but that doesn't mean water rights should be administered by anything other than the prior appropriation doctrine.

Idaho water law was in transition in the early 1990s. The Musser case was a turning point in the change from a past that promoted full development of the resource to a future that includes protecting public interests, managing ground and surface water sources as one, and consideration of the value of water to fish and wildlife.

The nineteenth century idea that water in the stream is free to be fully appropriated had been whittled away over the years.

The state's hydrologic studies of the aquifer enabled the Department of Water Resources to construct a computer model that shows the area in which pumpers most directly affect the spring flows that in turn affect the river. The model outlines strips of land about two and a half miles wide along the north and south banks of the American Falls Reservoir where pumping reduces the spring flows to the river — and the Twin Falls Canal Company water right — within six months or less of the time of the pumping. Over time, state officials refined the model to more closely resemble reality. The canal company still faced the difficulty of proving harm from any individual new irrigation well; only the cumulative effects were measurable. But that was the idea behind the computer model and the groundwater management area it defined: It could show the combined effects of all pumping within the area.

Idaho farmers base their investments and stake their livelihoods and the security of their families on the premise that water to which they hold a right will continue to be available, nature providing. A water right is a valuable property right, and such rights are bought, sold and held as collateral for farm loans. But the state shook that foundation when it tried to subordinate Idaho Power's senior water right, and by failing to protect the senior water rights of Alvin and Tim Musser and the Twin Falls Canal Company. If the state or the water right holder cannot protect the right, it is no longer a viable basis for credit and the security of farm operations. The fundamental principle behind prior appropriation is to ensure and promote certainty — bankable, creditworthy certainty. Anything that erodes a water right — whether drought, geologic change, development or other water rights — also erodes that certainty.

Despite the efforts of the state to create more rules, the decline in the aquifer level will continue as long as water users keep taking more water out of the aquifer than nature and farming practices add. Every time someone uses groundwater, the level goes down. When it drops below the outlet of a spring, that spring stops flowing. Nevertheless, the aquifer outflow at Thousand Springs still is higher than historic levels, though not uniformly.

U.S. Geological Survey figures show water is withdrawn from the aquifer in excess of recharge at a rate of more than four hundred thousand acre-feet of water per year. The advent of irrigation in southern Idaho diverted water from the Snake River out over the plain. Some of that water seeped down into the aquifer, and spring flows feeding water back to the Snake River grew steadily until the 1950s. Irrigators turned to pumps to supplement their surface water supplies to expand into areas not readily accessible to gravity irrigation. In other areas farmers began to line canals with concrete to reduce seepage losses. Others changed from flood irrigation to sprinklers. The net result was an increased demand on the aquifer and less recharge.

The Thousand Springs reach provides a visible indication, and one the U.S. Geological Survey has been keeping an eye on for many years. USGS data show that the level of the aquifer is generally independent of drought, but closely follows the advent of irrigation and new pump technology. From 1900 until about 1950, the spring discharge increased steadily from about 4,200 cubic feet per second to about 6,800 cubic feet per second. It has declined steadily ever since. Dry years and wet years have resulted in pulses in the springs' discharge, but the downward trend has held steady. In 1990 it was at 5,500 cubic feet. But that is still more than 1900 levels.

The effects of irrigation in earlier years in eastern Idaho on the springs in the American Falls reach is not as clear. In 1900, the Snake River carried enough water to supply the Twin Falls and North Side canal company water rights. Even after irrigation diversions began to dry up the river at Blackfoot, springs recharged the river enough to fill the canal company's right, long before Julian Clawson brought deep-well pumps to eastern Idaho. The unanswered question, the question that makes canal company manager Vince Alberdi uncomfortable, is how much water the springs in the American Falls reach discharge before irrigation began in eastern Idaho in the 1870s? The computer models and present conditions suggest flows from those springs alone would be enough to fill the canal company's water right.

If the aquifer runs short, that could spark a battle more contentious than Swan Falls.

Through the middle to late 1990s, the water supply in southern Idaho was mostly adequate. But a dry year in 2001, as it always does, brought the groundwater issue to a head. The Twin Falls Canal Company participated in the process and waited for the state to complete conjunctive management rules. The company was reluctant to issue a call for water. As a result, more and more the company was forced to rely on stored water, for which it had to pay.

Groundwater pumpers were reluctant to give ground—yes they were junior, but they refused to acknowledge that anyone could say which wells should be shut off. The lag time of groundwater flow gave them refuge and a loophole big enough to drive a beet truck through. Shutting off a pumper when the springs in American Falls began to go down might not revive those flows until after the irrigation season was over, resulting in a futile call for that year. Lawyers for the junior pumpers put up a fight, saying as long as there was no way to show that the individual pumpers were at fault, it would be unfair to shut them down.

But that argument was getting threadbare, and it no longer concealed the need for a real solution, senior water users complained. They were still going dry. And state courts already had ruled that the prior appropriation doctrine still applies to conjunctive management. Indeed, managing water rights in any way that doesn't follow prior appropriation could be considered a property right taking.

On July 13, 2001, the Twin Falls and North Side canal companies formally asked Water Resources Director Karl Dreher to designate a groundwater management area to allow increased control of pumping. Dreher, who holds a master's degree in civil engineering from Colorado State University, had been appointed by Governor Phil Batt to take over from Keith Higginson as director in 1995. State law gives the director authority to designate such an area if the water level is in danger of diminishing to a point where there isn't enough water to fill existing water rights. The designation gives the director the authority to shut off junior water rights when senior rights are going dry.

On August 3, 2001, over the objections of the groundwater pumpers, Dreher created two groundwater management areas—places where reduced spring flows meant water users were not getting their water. One area covered strips of land on both sides of the river from about five miles upstream of American Falls Reservoir to about six miles downstream. This was the area that affected the rights of the Twin Falls Canal Company. It also included the spot near Ferry Butte where Cassia County surveyor Frank Riblett in 1887 began his survey of irrigable lands along the river south and west past the Twin Falls and North Side tracts.

The other management area covered land north of the river, from a few miles west of Milner Dam downstream to King Hill. This area would affect the Musser water right and other irrigators in the Hagerman Valley and the trout hatcheries in the Snake River Canyon.

There were two sides in this fight. As Henry Schodde learned in 1908, a senior right is not always enough. He lost the fight to keep his water wheels operating with the current stilled by Milner Dam. The court, in a ruling applicable today, said that a water right holder has no absolute right to a means or method of diversion. The senior water user can be compelled to change that method, but the expense must be borne by junior users. Most found this argument reasonable.

Dreher warned water users that he would adopt the management areas, giving him authority to shut down junior pumpers. He would need to decide by August 28 whether junior water users would be shut off the following irrigation season. Curtailment notices had to be issued by September 1 to be legal for the following year. Department officials prepared notices to 1,300 groundwater users in 2002, based on priority and location within the groundwater management area. Domestic and small nonconsumptive uses were exempt. But the orders to shut off the pumps would not go out, Dreher noted, if the two sides could reach some agreement. The order also would be rescinded when the drought ended and senior rights were once again filled.

Dreher's action forced the groundwater pumpers to the table. Under threat of having their water shut off, irrigators in two groundwater areas agreed to cut back pumping or compensate senior water rights holders, in effect upholding prior appropriation.

For the Twin Falls Canal Company, the agreement would settle the long-running dispute with upstream groundwater pumpers. It would bring short-term relief and pave the way for a long-term solution to the contentious issue of managing ground and surface water together. The agreement recognized the seniority of the Twin Falls right over pumpers. The eastern Idaho pumpers agreed to replace depleted surface water up to 25,800 acre-feet annually, if available, or else curtail pumping by 15 percent, or a combination of the two.

Water users reached a similar agreement in the Thousand Springs reach, which supplies the Mussers' water right. Pumpers agreed to reduce pumping by forty thousand acre-feet per year. Everything seemed settled when the pumpers balked. They refused to sign. The deadline for the shut-off order loomed. State officials prepared notices to thirteen hundred pumpers. The notices were ready to go in the mail.

One hour before the deadline, the pumpers signed. Relief ran through southern Idaho like water down an irrigation ditch. But it was short-lived.

Director Dreher signed the order approving the agreements on January 18, 2002. Less than two months later, the department sent out notices warning of possible reductions in groundwater use during the coming irrigation season. The winter had brought less than average snow in the mountains again, and there was not enough water left in regional reservoirs to make up the difference. That meant groundwater pumpers would probably not be able to find enough surface water as compensation for senior water rights. And without replacement water, pumpers would have to cut back; the amount would depend on what water became available.

The problems and complexities that plagued the Twin Falls Canal Company and most other water users in southern Idaho, have their roots in the state's refusal to enforce the doctrine of prior appropriation, said former water judge Daniel Hurlbutt, who retired in December 1998. The doctrine is the simplest of laws. First in time is first in right. Water rights disputes would be easily settled if that simple doctrine were applied. But it requires an accurate record of water rights by priority date, place of use and purpose. Until the Snake River Basin Adjudication began in 1987 as part of the Swan Falls settlement, the state did not have an accurate, up-to-date record of water rights.

The application of the prior appropriation doctrine can have a harsh effect. For a hundred years, officials have shied away from the reality of shutting off a farmer simply because his or her water right was established a year, a month or a day later than someone else's. Rather than upholding the doctrine as required by the state's Constitution, water managers have found more water somewhere. They have tried to bend the Constitution with judicial decrees, rules and legislation. That has only created complexities, not solutions.

For Hurlbutt, that all raises the question: Why is the state, which is subject to political influence, allowed to administer the allocation of a public resource? To him that sounds oddly socialistic, especially for a state that purports to adhere to the capitalistic philosophy of a free and open marketplace. Perhaps it is the marketplace that should determine the price of water, and thus its allocation. Certainly no one knows better the value of water than the farmer with a wilting crop and ditches gone dry. But what if that farmer lives downstream from Idaho?

Courtesy Idaho Department of Water Resources
Siphon tubes take water from a ditch at the upper end of a field.

Chapter Fifteen:
Marketing Water

In late March 2001, just before the start of another irrigation season, Jon Bowling of the Idaho Power Company stood up at the front of an auditorium full of irrigators in Blackfoot and offered them $60 per acre-foot for any water they could spare. Bowling looked the part of a power company executive dressed casually to fit in with the roomful of John Deere and seed company caps. He seemed at ease, but his offer sent the irrigators buzzing like a hive of wild bees. The water he was looking for, to boost hydropower generation in a dry year, normally sold for $10 an acre-foot. But 2001 was looking like anything but a normal year. At $60 an acre-foot, it might pay some farmers, who used four to five acre-feet of water per acre, not to farm and instead rent their water to Idaho Power. They could make as much as $300 an acre by leaving their land dry.

Bowling's offer was part of Idaho Power's attempts to keep its seventeen Snake River hydroelectric turbines spinning during what everyone assumed would be a dry summer. When water in the river is low, the utility makes up part of the difference by buying power on the volatile wholesale power market. But deregulation and manipulation of that market had sent the cost of a megawatt of power from the usual $35 to $350. Renting water to run through the hydro plants would be cheaper than buying power on the open market.

Twin Falls Canal Company manager Vince Alberdi and board members Wayne Lincoln and Chuck Coiner had driven the two hours to Blackfoot that morning to hear what Bowling had to say. They, too, anticipated a dry year and wanted to rent some extra water. The canal company faced the prospect of cutting deliveries by a third if supplies didn't improve. That had happened only once before—in 1992—since American Falls Dam had been completed in 1927. During other dry years in the past, the company had cut back, but never by that much. Alberdi, Lincoln and Coiner, like many others who depended on rented water, feared they would have to bid against Idaho Power to get fifty thousand acre-feet of water from the state water bank. On their minds was the possibility that they were looking at the future—a future in which water allocation would be controlled by economic forces, a true "free market," instead of state authorities. They foresaw that opening the door a little wider to water markets would inject economic reality into what had been a closed allocation system that all but ignored the real cost of water. The power company's offer raised a question many had considered but few had voiced. Could water markets, with appropriate safeguards for existing uses, improve efficiency of water allocation? Could a system be fashioned that would respect the prior appropriation doctrine and satisfy competing needs for fish, hydropower, and recreation, as well as irrigation?

The "water bank" from which Idaho Power and the canal company both sought water is, in fact, a limited, temporary water market, but operated under the authority of the state Water Resources Board with rules that favor irrigators. "The water bank is our insurance policy," Coiner said. The canal company often relied on the state water bank to get through dry years when supplies were short. In recent years, the bank also had become a source of the water that eastern Idaho groundwater pumpers would tap to compensate the canal company for the effects that pumping had on the company's senior water right.

In the simplest terms, water users who have more water than they require put the excess in the bank. Water from the bank can then be rented to people who don't have enough. The risk is that renting water leaves little for next year if the winter is dry and reservoirs don't fill. Storage space for water rented out one year is considered the last to fill the following year.

In general, a water bank responds to short-term variations in the supply. The bank sets rental rates and rules that limit the conditions of rental, including the kinds and places of use, to protect other water users.

The first water bank on the upper Snake River in eastern Idaho was casual and unofficial. The practice began during the Dust Bowl drought in the 1930s. In 1932, 14,700 acre-feet of water was rented out for seventeen cents per acre-foot. In 1934, the amount rose to 40,000 acre-feet at twenty-five cents a foot. In following years, the price rose until it reached seventy-five cents a foot in 1978. The process eventually was formalized with legislation in 1979, adopting a recommendation set out in the state's 1976 water plan. It was the first permanent water bank in the arid West. It is managed for the Water Resources Board by the Committee of Nine.

A second water bank, in the Boise Basin, was established in 1988, and a third, in 1990, in the Payette River drainage. The Shoshone-Bannock Tribe on the Fort Hall Reservation also operates a separate bank.

The Water Resources Board must approve the operating rules and rental rates adopted by the Committee of Nine. In 2001, the standard rate was $2.95 per acre-foot for water diverted above Milner Dam. For water used below Milner, beyond the reach of the irrigators and the committee's authority, the charge was $10.50, in part to discourage transfer of water out of the basin. The Snake River above Milner was legally considered separately from the river below the dam. Ten percent of the rental fee goes to pay administrative costs and to fund a loan and grant program that is used to finance water projects. The rest goes to the person who puts the water up for rent.

Idaho Power's offer ran into one of the fundamental water bank rules. Water can't be leased for use below Milner until other upstream irrigation requests have been filled. The utility had hoped to encourage people to deposit water in the bank, but it was a self-defeating effort. It had the opposite effect, actually removing the incentive to put water in the water bank. Why offer water for rent at $2.95, when later, after irrigation needs were met, there was a potential to rent that same water for $60? Regardless of Idaho Power's dangling carrot, the rules required the water bank to fill requests for irrigation needs as deposits were made.

Jon Bowling was offering enough to tempt some irrigators to mortgage long-term stability of the water bank for short-term gain. But it quickly became clear that the implications of a proposed change in water bank rules to accommodate the offer were anything but clear. Earlier in March, in anticipation of Idaho Power's offer, the Committee of Nine had changed its rules to allow irrigators to negotiate higher rental fees when there was no water in the rental pool. The change also would allow Idaho Power to offer more for the water in a year of water shortage. The new rule would allow such a sale only during special circumstance and at a negotiated rate, District One water master Ron Carlson said. The water would not go into the water bank rental pool. The rule still faced approval by the Water Resources Board.

But some irrigators expressed concern that the change would unravel the water bank, opening the state to water marketing, pitting water users against each other and against outside users. If farmers rented stored water to Idaho Power, they could price their neighbors out of the market. Water users, including the Twin Falls Canal Company, feared water would no longer go to senior water rights holders but to the highest bidders.

The idea of renting water bumped hard against the prior appropriation doctrine's use-it-or-lose-it clause. Technically, a water right under the doctrine is defined by the amount of water that can be put to an officially recognized beneficial use. The right to any water not used for five years is lost. The right is only for the use of the water; it doesn't include ownership. Idaho Power wanted to rent only the right to use water that under other circumstances might have gone to junior water rights. But because the water in question was stored in federal reservoirs, priority rights did not strictly apply. The rules for stored water were more like contract law. Irrigators contracted with the Bureau of Reclamation for a certain amount of stored water collected during the winter and spring. That water might otherwise run downriver and through Idaho Power's hydroelectric turbines.

In April 2001, the Committee of Nine crowded into a stuffy meeting room in the Pocatello airport to hash out disagreements over the proposed rule change. Some favored the advantage of selling water to the highest bidder; others feared that would undercut the needs of agriculture. Some feared that allowing Idaho Power to bid for stored water would undermine the principles of the water bank and force irrigators to bid against the utility. The rule would let irrigators rent out water for short-term gains. But the storage reservoirs were meant to provide irrigation water, not profit for water-right holders, Alberdi said. "I don't think we can prostitute ourselves for short-term gains without long-term consequences," he said.

But this year was different, argued state Representative Del Raybould, an eastern Idaho Republican. This year natural flows and stored water would not be enough for some farmers to get through the season. The new rule would give them a way out by letting them dry up their land for the year and rent the water to Idaho Power or another high bidder.

After much heated discussion, the committee decided against Raybould and Carlson and those who sided with them. It was close, but committee members upheld the long-standing agricultural preference to all water in the water bank. They had withstood the temptation. Only when irrigation requests had been met could other requests for water below Milner be filled—including Idaho Power's request, regardless of what the utility offered. In years like 2001, that didn't leave much water. By the April meeting, irrigators already had asked the water bank for 261,588 acre-feet; Idaho Power had asked for 100,000 acre-feet for power generation below Milner Dam. But there was nothing in the bank.

Jon Bowling came away empty-handed, his trial balloon shot down. But he was not the first to come to southern Idaho to attempt a withdrawal from the upper Snake River water bank. In the early 1990s the Bonneville Power Administration and the Bureau of Reclamation came looking for water to help flush young endangered salmon to sea. The Bureau officials were more successful. They had offered only $20 per acre-foot versus Idaho Power's $60, but they owned the reservoirs. And the federal agencies had the clout of the Endangered Species Act to help wring some water out of the arid eastern Idaho lava plain. That effort had started ten years before Bowling showed up.

In the middle of 1992, one of the worst water years on record, John Keys, then Pacific Northwest regional director of the U.S. Bureau of Reclamation, wanted a hundred thousand acre feet of water to help migrating salmon.

He was met with disbelief. Some irrigators already were out of water. But Keys wouldn't take no for an answer. He couldn't. In 1991, the National Marine Fisheries Service listed Idaho sockeye salmon as a federal endangered species. Three runs of Chinook salmon would soon follow on the list as threatened. The federal government's salmon recovery plan, required by the Endangered Species Act, depended on water from southern Idaho. Federal officials charged with salmon recovery called for Idaho, Bonneville Power Administration and the Bureau to come up with the water through purchases or water conservation projects in the state.

In 1991, the Bureau had rented water from water banks on the upper Snake and Payette rivers as part of the Idaho Water Rental Pilot Project. The project was a cooperative effort by the Bonneville Power Administration, Idaho Department of Fish and Game, the Shoshone-Bannock Tribes and Idaho Power Company to study the effectiveness of renting water to increase flow through downstream reservoirs. The plan shifted flood control storage in Brownlee and Dworshak reservoirs to provide more water in the Snake River during the spring. It also called for lowering the levels in the lower Snake and Columbia river reservoirs to increase water velocity, speeding the young fish on their spring migration. Water from eastern Idaho would be needed later in the year.

In November 1991, the Bureau asked the state of Idaho for a temporary change in the water rights for its reservoirs to move 427,000 acre-feet down the Snake River when the salmon needed help on their annual migration. And 100,000 acre-feet of that would come from the upper Snake River reservoirs. Keys hoped to find enough irrigators with reservoir storage space or water from state water banks on the Boise, Snake and Payette rivers.

Irrigators simply didn't believe it at first, but the pressure was mounting. The Bonneville Power Administration—the federal agency that markets power from eight federal dams on the lower Snake and Columbia rivers—the aluminum industry, utilities and irrigators on the Corps of Engineers' reservoirs in Washington and

Oregon all were pointing accusing fingers at Idaho. They claimed Idaho was not doing its part to save the fish. They wanted Idaho to provide more water to help flush young fish on their spring migration to the ocean.

The real problem, however, is the eight federal dams on the lower Snake and Columbia rivers that block the passage of salmon on their way to and from the hundreds of miles of prime salmon spawning and rearing streams in central Idaho. Most fishery scientists agree that those dams, especially the four dams on the lower Snake River in southeastern Washington, are among the chief causes that have all but wiped out wild Idaho salmon and steelhead runs. Idaho irrigators were being asked to pay part of the cost of recovering the iconic fish. Oddly enough, they did not support the idea of breaching the dams on the lower Snake, which scientists say would be the best chance for recovering the salmon. If the dams were breached, water from Idaho wouldn't be needed for salmon recovery. But the same irrigators who once dried up the river at Milner Dam and Blackfoot accused federal agencies of having a single purpose, without any concern for agriculture. (The same could be said about irrigators: They seemed to have a single purpose that included no concern for fish.) But they also feared that if the dams were breached and the salmon still didn't recover, the federal government might use the endangered species act to wrest more water from southern and eastern Idaho.

Keys was caught in the middle. He was on the hook for a hundred thousand acre-feet before the end of August 1992 to help fall Chinook salmon and steelhead trout returning to the state.

Meanwhile that summer, farmers in eastern Idaho with water rights dating to 1895 already were having their water shut off. It would turn out to be the worst water year since 1934, when National Guard troops were called out to guard head gates on diversions that had been shut off. Keys wanted to rent water from the water bank. He was willing to buy it if he could find someone willing to sell. That year the water bank had only 3,593 acre-feet of water available, and a lot of people already were in line ahead of him. By the time Keys showed up, the bank already had requests for 150,000 acre-feet, and water bank rules give first priority to irrigators. In a normal year the water bank would have had plenty of water. The year before, water managers had released 100,000 acre-feet from storage, expecting normal winter precipitation. They had no idea how bad 1992 would be.

Keys was undaunted.

"We're going to have to come up with some water," he said firmly, "even if it means some people will have to give something up. The Endangered Species Act can't take people's water if their diversions aren't harming the salmon. But when the National Marine Fisheries Service calls for water for salmon recovery, the Bureau may have no choice but to provide it and then somehow figure out how to compensate those who may have lost irrigation water."

Amazingly, he got the water he was looking for, and he continued to get it every year until he retired in 1998. But he had some help. The Idaho Legislature became involved in making the temporary water supplies available for downstream use. Idaho water law requires legislative approval if more than fifty cubic feet, or five thousand acre-feet are diverted from any basin in the state. "The Bureau of Reclamation worked closely with Senate President Laird Noh, House Speaker Bruce Newcomb, the Idaho water Resources Board, Keith Higginson, Governor Andrus, the water users and other for passage of the state law that allows for the purchase, diversion and use," Keys said years later.

It was a temporary, year-to-year fix, and Keys hoped to make the change permanent. But there was no existing mechanism, short of annual rentals from the water bank, to transfer water downstream, essentially as an instream water right. Under existing Idaho law, only the state Water Resources Board could hold an instream water right. The difficulty originates with the prior appropriation doctrine that is based on the idea of diverting water from a stream and putting it to some "beneficial" use. Though there may be public benefits, Idaho law doesn't consider leaving water in the river as putting it to use.

The Bureau considered buying back some storage space in the reservoirs. The reservoirs were authorized by Congress for irrigation and built with tax dollars, but needs had changed since they were built, Keys said. Buying back space may seem needlessly expensive, but it would be cheaper than building new storage reservoirs. And renting water from year to year, increasingly was seen as a threat by irrigators competing for the same water.

The Bureau's long-term plans, however, made Idaho irrigators' blood run cold. By 1999, the options under consideration included a study of the effects of taking 1.4 million acre-feet of water from upper Snake River reservoirs for increased salmon flows. Taking that much water out of eastern Idaho could shut down irrigation on 350,000 acres. The government plans cast clouds of uncertainty over irrigators with the Twin Falls Canal Company. The recovery plan might not take water directly from the canal company, but a lot of it is spread on land and helps recharge the groundwater that feeds the springs in the upper end of the American Falls Reservoir, which in turn make up the canal company's water right.

In an average year, about 1.5 million acre-feet flow past Milner Dam, but most of that is at a time when the salmon don't need it. Taking 1.4 million acre-feet would put a serious dent in the four million acre-feet of storage capacity in the federal upper Snake River reservoirs. Worst of all, irrigators said they were not convinced that the water would bring the salmon back from the brink of extinction.

Scientists mostly agreed that the flows wouldn't, by themselves, bring the salmon back, but until other more effective measures could be put in place, the extra water would help buy the fish some time.

The Idaho Water Users Association didn't disagree with the idea of Idaho helping salmon recovery. But the Bureau of Reclamation needed to demonstrate that the water would actually benefit the fish, that it was in the public interest and that sources in other states had been developed, association executive director Sherl Chapman said. He wanted to make sure that the Bureau wasn't just throwing water at the problem with the assumption that it would work. Biologists ought to be able to tell whether the 427,000 acre-feet of water from Idaho would actually help the fish. And before any water was sent out of Idaho, Chapman wanted the state to make sure the water would actually be used to help the fish and that moving it would not harm local economies and water rights holders in Idaho. He wanted to ensure that downstream interests weren't just using the water to generate power.

The issue would test the political might of irrigators. For more than a century, they had held a lock on water in southern Idaho.

In part, they were protecting a good thing, but there was more to it. For most irrigators, water was cheap. Increased competition from the outside for rented water would eventually drive up the price, moving control out of the hands of the irrigation bureaucracy.

At the Snake River Symposium in Twin Falls in 1982, water lawyer John Rosholt predicted the future of water management in Idaho. On its way through southern Idaho, the water in the Snake River drives hydroelectric turbines and irrigates nearly one million acres of farmland. Agriculture grew up alongside electric power generation in the state's early days, but the dominant use of water may not always be irrigating that land, said Rosholt, who represents the Twin Falls Canal Company.

"Water follows dollars," he said.

The four and a half acre-feet of water the average southern Idaho farmer uses per acre of cropland could generate more revenue if it were run through Idaho Power's Snake River hydroelectric dams—in 2001 the company was willing to pay $60 per acre-foot for excess water to run down the river. That same water spread on land in the Columbia basin where the growing season is at least thirty days longer, and the soil is deeper and needs less water, could grow nearly twice as many potatoes as the upper Snake River Basin. And that's after it has run through the gantlet of hydro plants. In the future, the demand for water may dictate that it be used only where it can be used most efficiently, Rosholt predicted.

That may not happen for a number of years, but the time surely will come, he said. Instead of people in southern Idaho farming irrigated lands, they may work at trout farms, power plants, geothermal stations, refineries and even oil fields if investors were willing to drill in excess of twelve thousand feet. Okay, perhaps the oil wells were less likely until prices came back up, Rosholt said at the time. But the essence of water marketing is moving water to its highest economic use, and that is the future of water management in Idaho, he said.

It hasn't come true yet. Today in Idaho, water still is allocated by institutions established when water was considered a free resource. Even in desperately dry years—like 1977 and 1992—water in southern Idaho sold for next to nothing. Snake River water is some of the cheapest in the West, thanks in part to the largesse of the federal government that built and operates the reservoirs on the upper Snake River. Irrigators can get water stored in federal reservoirs for as little as twelve cents an acre-foot—that's enough to supply an average family of four for a year. Twin Falls Canal Company shareholders were paying $18 per share at the start of the twenty-first century. The $18 paid for about four acre-feet delivered to the farmer's head gate. That pencils out to $4.50 per acre-foot. Still a pretty good deal for a commodity that is essential to agriculture in the arid West. An irrigator upstream of Milner Dam can rent an acre-foot for $2.95. At that rate, a penny buys eleven hundred gallons. Meanwhile, Las Vegas early in the twenty-first century was paying $3,200 per acre-foot.

Even under these circumstances, Idaho Power was unable to rent any water despite offering $60 per acre-foot. Not exactly free market economics. But even an open market has its disadvantages.

"We wouldn't buy much water for salmon at $3,200 an acre-foot," John Keys lamented.

But that may well be the future.

The water market Rosholt predicted in 1982 would certainly encourage water users to manage the resource more carefully, both in order to pay less for the water they need and to sell any they could save. Throughout the West, cheap water and the prior appropriation doctrine have conspired to discourage conservation. Irrigators who pay the same low rate per acre or per share regardless of how much water they actually use have no reason to conserve. Nor would they get to keep any water they actually save. Under the prior appropriation doctrine, any water saved through increased efficiency or simply careful water management is technically not part of a legitimate water right. That encourages some farmers to use as much as they are entitled to, for fear their rights could be curtailed—not because they need it, but because they might lose it.

Even so, water conservation in the Snake River Basin is an illusion, of sorts. It cannot increase the amount of water in the basin. But it can improve the efficiency of its use. The only real changes have been where it flows and when. Over the years, as diversions from the Snake River have decreased and groundwater pumping has increased, flows from springs along the Snake River Canyon have decreased. But the flow at the U.S. Geological Survey gauging station at King Hill, downstream of those springs, hasn't shown any significant change. It corresponds to the Heise gauging station on the Snake River upstream of eastern Idaho irrigation diversions. Both rise and fall with irrigation seasons and precipitation. Changes in diversions and in groundwater pumping have altered the balance and the time the water shows up, not the total amount of water.

Like conservation measures, an open water market wouldn't make more water available in the Snake River Basin. But by providing economic incentives for increased efficiency, such a market might make allocation more fair, and might create a way to provide water for instream flows that would generate electricity and provide water for recreation, aesthetics and salmon and other fish and wildlife. Water bank transfers help, but they are temporary and only when water is available.

A water market might raise the cost of extra water for the Twin Falls Canal Company, especially in dry years, when prices would be driven up by increased bidding by outside interests, such as cities with growing needs. But it might also inspire company managers to improve efficiency. That's something they already are working on. As they wear out, many canal control structures are replaced with computer-controlled mechanisms. A central computer makes the job of adjusting the flow to respond to irrigation demands and problems much quicker. No longer do the canals need to run at full volume all the time. Ditch riders no longer need to drive out to change flow settings. These changes already have increased the efficiency of the company's water use.

Certainly a market raises some issues, even if applied within the framework of the prior appropriation system and existing water rights. In a sense it already exists in limited form. Dairy owners in southern Idaho who want to expand their operations, for example, buy water rights from farmers willing to dry up their farmland. The holder of a water right now has a right to sell that right to the highest bidder, with some restrictions to protect other rights. The trouble with water rights is they are not as readily definable as a plot of land. They vary with supply and need according to seniority, which makes older rights more valuable.

And they don't exist in isolation. Selling a right can affect other water rights. Unlike water bank transactions that are temporary, the transfer of a water right can affect local economies and social structure. When water rights are transferred, any change in use, time or place of use, must be approved by the Department of Water Resources. Such changes may affect the ability of other users to obtain otherwise legitimate water rights. Changes also affect incidental benefits, such as recreation and fish and wildlife habitat. Moving water downstream, however, would provide instream flows regardless of the source or purpose.

The federal government's purchase of water to help flush endangered salmon to the ocean, or Idaho Power's purchase for power generation, provide improved recreation flows and help improve water quality and aesthetic values. In fact, leaving water in the river may be the biggest indirect benefit of such transfers.

Water users hold only usufruct rights to a certain amount of water. They don't own it. And yet in one instance, federal requirements to provide some public use of public water resulted in at least indirect private gain. Until the last decade of the twentieth century, the river at Milner Dam was fully appropriated—that is zero flow was accepted state policy. Only in the winter and spring and in a few high flow years did water pass Milner. When the dam was rebuilt in the early 1990s, the Federal Energy Regulatory Commission required a minimum flow of two hundred cubic feet past the dam, but only when the water was available. Idaho Power, which built and operates the power plant that was incorporated in the rebuilt dam, would supply the water. Irrigators and then-canal company manager Jack Eakin noted that the utility would need to buy that water from the water bank. But water in the water bank would come from irrigators in the Snake River Valley. So irrigators successfully negotiated a solution that in effect put money in their own pockets while supplying a minimum flow required by the federal government for public benefits. That, perhaps, is a small example of the potential of a water market, and an example of a potential incentive to conserve water if it could then be sold.

Existing demand for whitewater recreation offers some justification for market scenarios that would provide substantial recreation flows. With ten thousand cubic feet per second churning in the reach below Milner Dam, the river would become one of the most challenging whitewater runs in the country. The word spreads quickly and whitewater boaters come from all over the world to run the Milner and the Murtaugh reaches. A beneficial use you say? Old-time irrigators stand on the canyon rim and shake their heads at the crazed young men defying certain death in their brightly colored plastic boats.

Former Idaho water judge Daniel Hurlbutt asks: Is it right for the state to control the administration and allocation of a limited and valuable public resource? Is it reasonable that all water should go first to irrigated agriculture? Is it reasonable that an open market should have a role in allocating water, especially in a strongly Republican state that prides itself in its capitalistic ideal of economic forces free from government meddling?

It seems an open market in water could be a gold mine for some. Water is worth a lot of money, and it will only increase in value as demand and competition grow. Water may be worth even more farther downstream where growing seasons are longer and the water runs through a string of power plants, as John Rosholt suggests. It also seems clear that in an open market, water would go to the highest bidder, not necessarily the senior water right holder. Water, as they say, would flow toward money. The market, not the community or social institutions, would determine the highest and best use of water. Is that the best way to protect the public interest? Perhaps not. An open market puts the resource at risk of unscrupulous exploitation and speculation, holding hostage farmers and communities, and everyone who depends on a reliable source of water.

And water is, after all, a public resource.

Does it make sense to protect the low cost of water for a select group? And if a market is created for water rights, who should profit from the sale of rights that many paid little or nothing for? Would the public have a say in how and where the water is used?

Would the public share in any profit through royalties? If Las Vegas is paying $3,200 an acre-foot, what might other cities pay in the future? And who should profit from the sale of rights to water in federally subsidized reservoirs?

It doesn't seem unreasonable for the public to expect that some water should serve other public interests, the same way some land is retained as open space for parks. Certainly it would be in the public interest to leave some water for recreation, aesthetics, for wild salmon and the birds of the Deer Flat National Wildlife Refuge. They serve interests that have no easily discernable dollar value, yet their contribution to our quality of life is inestimable.

Without a doubt, a water market could widen the allocation of a limited resource. It would require appropriate rules that respect existing users, so that one sale doesn't make other rights useless. Such rules would have to adapt to the doctrine of prior appropriation, and they would have to consider long-term effects. A freer market might loosen the irrigators' grip on control of the resource, but it would increase efficiency. Water would move downstream to other uses, helping to improve water quality, and providing whitewater recreation opportunities and water for hydropower generation, as well as water for irrigation.

Some irrigators, however, already see demands on the resource for water quality, recreation, fish and wildlife as attacks on their water rights, rights that have never been questioned as they are today. Some see the solution as taking control of water away from state and federal bureaucrats and putting it in the hands of economic forces. Others say that may be too risky. In a sense they are right to worry. If farmers have to bid against Idaho Power for some or all of their irrigation water, they may as well sell their water rights.

A water market could unravel the fabric of rural society in the arid West that the likes of I.B. Perrine helped to weave, unless it respects the priority of water rights and the incidental values of water. Arguably, not all existing uses of water deserve protection. But creating a mechanism for frugal water users to benefit from conservation could provide a lot of water that now is simply wasted. And the value of water extends beyond economics. Twin Falls Canal Company shareholders may not pay a lot for their wa-

ter, but that water does more than raise potatoes, beans and alfalfa. It molds a group of farmers into a community in ways that
simply can't be calculated in dollars.

Courtesy Twin Falls Canal Co.
Engineers inspect the tunnel gates that would divert the main flow of
the Snake River during construction of Milner Dam.

Chapter Sixteen:
Common Source of Prosperity

Early Wednesday morning, June 2, 1999, Wayne Goetz, a farmer who lives near the High Line Canal about six miles south of the town of Kimberly, heard the sound of rushing water. When he went to investigate, he saw water gushing from a hole fifteen feet across at the base of the High Line Canal bank. He could hear the rush of water from a quarter mile away. Goetz called the Twin Falls Canal Company office just before 7 a.m. to report the break. Canal company officials spread the word on the company radio. Company manager Vince Alberdi heard the radio call just as he was about to leave home, dressed for the office. His heart thumping, he headed straight out to the scene. He didn't even stop to change his shoes.

That morning the High Line Canal carried about fifteen hundred cubic feet per second of water, about half the company's natural water right. Alberdi estimated that about 34,000 to 36,000 gallons per minute were leaking through the canal bank around a pipeline that crossed under the canal. The leak threatened to breach the canal bank, threatening homes, farmlands and roads on lands below the canal. And it threatened the irrigation water supply to nearly half the 202,000-acre Twin Falls tract, including some of the farthest reaches. Shutting off the High Line would affect the operation of the entire canal system.

Even as Alberdi was on his way to the scene, the company's emergency response had swung into action. Trucks were dispatched to haul large rock. Flow in the High Line and the rest of the system back to Milner Dam was cut back. Crews were called out to the leak. But it takes time to mobilize and start hauling material to a break. When Alberdi arrived, the situation still looked rugged. But already dump trucks were beginning to line up to dump their loads.

Everyone with a serviceable dump truck showed up to help. One driver from the nearby town of Filer, who worked for Idaho Sand and Gravel, spent most of his time waiting in line atop the canal bank. He pulled leisurely on a cigarette as he waited to dump his load. His was one of thirty-two, ten-yard dump trucks that during the day hauled four hundred yards of rock, twenty-two hundred yards of dirt and twenty-five to thirty tons of bentonite clay to plug the hole in the canal bank. Gathered around the break like giant, frantic mechanical beavers, three tracked excavators and a bulldozer moved the rocks, bentonite and dirt brought by the steady pipeline of dump trucks.

For Alberdi that day spoke volumes about the community that has grown up around the canal company he runs, a company built on a foundation of cooperation. People did not hesitate to drop their own jobs to help when the call went out. Here, as elsewhere in the arid West, rural economies depend on farming, and farming depends on adequate and dependable irrigation facilities.

The Wild West was tamed, not by rugged individualists with six-guns, but by determined men with slide rules and irrigation shovels—and by legions of farmers willing to work together. Folks here like to consider themselves an independent lot in this rock-ribbed Republican stronghold that espouses the benefits of free market economics and the sanctity of the rights of the individual. But in reality the federal government made settlement of the West possible, continues to make irrigation water supplies dependable, and keeps many farmers afloat with crop subsidies. As the American historian and writer Bernard De Voto noted, all the rugged individualists in the old West were hung at the end of rope. At the other end of that rope were all the people whose lives depend on cooperation, the people who drive the bulldozers and dump trucks, who pour the concrete, the surveyors who peer through the glass of a transit, and the farmers who raise crops.

Building Milner Dam and the Twin Falls canal system, an effort beyond the scope of individual or small groups of farmers, required the combined efforts of hundreds of people. Only by working together did farmers then have the resources to operate and maintain the irrigation system, keep the canals clean and repair major breaks. They worked together against invading pests and to maintain legal rights to the water. The Twin Falls canal system would not have been built without the surveys of Frank Riblett and John Hansen, the vision of Bert Perrine and the investments of Stanley Milner and Frank Buhl. But they would have gotten nowhere without the men and women who bought the land and paid for their water shares, who put their sweat into building the system, and who continue to make the system work. Many of the early settlers who bought shares in the Twin Falls canal project put everything they had into it. Many took temporary jobs, working on the dam or the canals, until the water reached their newly acquired fields. Some got rich. Most made a decent living. A few went broke.

Whoever controlled the water, controlled this common source of prosperity. In Idaho, that control was tightly held by irrigators, and mostly it still is. But water users had to cooperate among themselves, and they had to cooperate with water users up and down the river. The Twin Falls canal system is designed on the basis of mutual dependence.

Brian Olmstead, who farms south of Twin Falls, and Wayne Lincoln, who farms about ten miles to the west, depend on the water from the canal system. Neither one gets any water if the farmers at the end of the system, like Terry Kramer who farms in Castleford, don't get their share. The canal system is designed to carry a maximum of about 3,500 cubic feet per second, and it can carry up to 3,800 in a pinch. But it only works when it's full, or nearly full. So when the water level drops significantly, no one gets any water. Anything that affects the level of water in the canal, affects everyone on the system and the entire community. And membership in the irrigation system makes them interdependent. They are not customers who contract with a federal bureaucracy for water deliveries. They own the dam and the canals and laterals that deliver their water. They own the ditch riders' pickup trucks and the heavy equipment used to repair and maintain the entire system. And if the dam or a canal bank breaks, and threatens everyone on the system, they have to fix it.

It was an unusual break, Alberdi said that June day, standing in a driving rain on the bank that rose more than twenty feet above the nearby fields, the strain written on his face. When he arrived, the telltale vortex, normally seen near the site of a leak in a canal bank, was missing. That meant the leak had to be deep under the middle of the canal. Alberdi was concerned about a pipeline that passed beneath the canal. Repairing the canal risked damaging the pipe below it. But the leak had to be stopped. If the pipeline were damaged, it could be repaired later.

(The Williams Pipeline is not part of the canal system; it moves water pumped out of nearby Rock Creek to land above the High Line Canal. The crews would make the best repairs that would get the system through the irrigation season. They would refill the trench along the pipeline and compact the dirt to rebuild the canal bank. Once the leak was stopped and the damage to the canal bank repaired, workers would send a remote video camera up inside the pipe to look for leaks or damage. Later, after the irrigation season that year, the pipe would be suspended above the canal to prevent future problems.)

Alberdi wasn't sure what had caused the canal break — a leak in the pipeline, or a leak in the canal bottom along the pipeline. If water moved through the canal bank, there must have been a void; if there was a void, the pipe must have moved. The pipe might have moved when the pump that forced water through it started and stopped. But freezing and thawing over the winter might also have been the source of trouble. Another canal company manager suggested that with the past snowless winter, the expansion and contraction of the steel pipe with the cold could have caused a void in the dirt around it. Whatever caused the problem, when the canal filled that spring, water seeped into cracks in the bottom of the canal and down around the outside of the pipe. Eventually water flowed along the pipe and gradually eroded enough dirt to start a serious leak — serious enough that it nearly took out the canal bank.

With the whine of hydraulic pumps, trucks dumped large rocks into the breach that had started to gnaw away at the canal bank. Other trucks dumped smaller rock and then gravel. Then two or three trucks dumped their loads of bentonite clay into the hole. About two minutes later, with the bentonite mixed into a slurry like wet cement in the hole, the leak slowed to a trickle and then all but stopped. But not before a few tense moments passed. "It was nip and tuck there for little while," Alberdi said over the grumble of diesel engines working with single-minded determination at plugging the leak.

The threat of a canal break always looms during the irrigation season. "When the water is in, it's like—you just never know," Alberdi said. "I guess it's like being a fireman. You never know when the call is going to come in." Luckily, this one happened on a rainy day when farmers didn't need the water. On a hot summer day, it could have been catastrophic for a lot of farmers. That's one of the pressures that come with the job, Alberdi said. By evening, the leak was sealed. It caused no serious damage, but the next day the real work would begin, finding and resolving the problem and then making repairs. Alberdi headed out to the canal one more time before going home for the day. Everything looked as it should, but he was going to have to buy a new pair of shoes.

Water, and especially the control of water, defines the arid West, and nobody knows better than irrigators how tenuous that control can be. That's as true today as it was in 1905. Water developments, starting with the Spanish settlers in the late sixteenth century, made permanent settlement possible in many otherwise inhospitable places. In Idaho, as elsewhere, water was the key resource. Settlers only needed a way to divert it.

The peculiarities of topography in southern Idaho made inexpensive gravity irrigation possible. Geologic forces shaped the land with its gentle slope from mountains in Wyoming to the lower, fertile, tillable lands to the west. In between, the landscape also held many suitable sites for reservoirs strategically upslope from the arable lands. A few miles east of Twin Falls, the land provided a convenient place where the Snake River could be diverted.

Early surveyors laid out the lines for irrigation canals that hugged the contours of the land. Eastern financiers provided the money to build the diversion and distribution works. The federal

1894 Carey Act made the land available. And visionary I. B. Perrine brought them all together. The Twin Falls project occupies a significant place in the history of western water development. It undermined a lot of resistance to the Carey Act, and it disproved skeptics who asserted that only the federal government could successfully build large-scale irrigation systems. Against the odds, private investors built an irrigation company comparable to anything the federal government could do at the time. In 1900, when proposed, the Twin Falls project was the largest of its kind in the country. It became the showcase of the Carey Act, eclipsed in later years only by monumental federal projects funded by taxpayers.

From 1903 to 1905, the project transformed Robert Stuart's wormwood forest to the beginnings of a verdant, irrigated agricultural Eden. By 1910, the population of the newly created Twin Falls County had grown from a few handfuls to more than 13,500 souls. The project attracted more than $24 million in investments. It brought $40 million into the southern Idaho economy in the first fifteen years. The canal system was built with the help of steam and electric power, by men with horses, picks and shovels and mule-drawn scrapers. Now it is controlled largely by a computer system, with remote sensors and automatic gates. And someday soon, water will be available on demand, delivered by computerized ditch riders who manage head gates on more than 1,000 miles of laterals and ditches from the comfort of an office.

Overcoming the vagaries of nature with technology would perhaps provide a more reliable water supply, but that should not be mistaken for an improvement upon nature. It is naïve to think that science could improve on nature. For as Vince Alberdi and the rest of the members of the Twin Falls Canal Company have seen firsthand, the illusion of control is temporary. He recognizes that irrigators can adapt the system to human use, but always at a cost. They may have brought water to the land, but no one tamed the arid country. At best they learned to live with its exacting demands. And periodically drought returns, and canal banks spring leaks lest, they forget.

Irrigation development assumes that bringing water to the desert is a good thing, and perhaps it is. But consider the costs. The land once supported more than seven hundred species of plants, from small flowers to sagebrush taller than a man. Diverting water does more than just dry up a river; it removes the very essence of the river. When the water is taken, the fish, beaver, muskrat, otter, insects, invertebrates and aquatic plants all are evicted. They are as much part of what make a river a river as the water. Thus, there is a purpose in terming the sagebrush steppe an unproductive desert, a wasteland devoid of all but the hardiest, toughest forms of life—a land where only irrigation could make the desert bloom. The underlying philosophy held that land was not considered productive if it was not producing wealth for its owners. Irrigation was seen as a way to make the land productive, even if that meant drying up the river.

But here, irrigation built an economy with the water, an economy that has supported the city of Twin Falls and smaller towns in the surrounding region for a century. In its early days, it was a hard-working town that had little time or energy for aesthetics and expected the same of the river from whence it drew its livelihood. In fact, folks hereabouts, in apparent justification, still consider the Snake River a "working river." They have worked it near to death. Runoff from irrigated agriculture and from dairies and feedlots, fish hatchery effluents, municipal sewage plant discharges and hydroelectric development have left this river a weed-choked shadow of its former self.

In the days of I.B. Perrine and John Hayes, Charlie Walgamott and John Hansen, early dreamers, standing close to where Robert Stuart stood, envisioned a town overlooking scenic Rock Creek Canyon. But the town turned away. Only in later years, a few residents cleaned up the garbage of a century, and the city built a walking trail along the creek. But the distinctive odor of sewage still lingers.

Sadly, the city that depends for its existence on irrigation water does not commemorate the opening of the canal system with any kind of annual celebration. Nor does it celebrate the coming of the railroad that made the newly irrigated farms profitable. Abundant water and the control of water may have made agriculture possible here, but the success of the Twin Falls tract is closely tied to the railroads that hauled thousands of carloads of soon-to-be famous Idaho potatoes to the rest of the country.

The future of this irrigation community now rests on how well its members meet coming challenges and whether they accept responsibility for effects of their past activities. Oppressive clouds hang over the future of the Twin Falls Canal Company as competition for the water supply in the Eastern Snake River Plain Aquifer intensifies. It's an issue the state will be forced to resolve if agriculture and the canal company are to survive. And it's an issue that will come to a head when the canal company makes a call for its water—if it's not already too late. For without water, the economy of south-central Idaho would crumble. If they survive at all, the farmers on the Twin Falls tract, who depend on the water of the Snake River, will continue to live with the uncertainties of water in the West. Balanced between the available water and competing uses, between what nature deals and what crops require, between what the law allows and what can be wrung from the land, life here is never far from the edge and never out of sight of the importance of water.

Harnessed, but not entirely tamed, the river still flows out onto the arid land, raising hopes enough each spring to plant another crop.

Courtesy Idaho Department of Water Resources
Some farmers use sprinklers to improve efficiency and water quality.

Epilogue:
The Battle Continues

In January of 2005, the winter snowpack held faint promise for the coming irrigation season, and a string of dry years had left little in the federal reservoirs on the Snake River. Southern Idaho appeared to be heading into the sixth consecutive year of drought. Unless spring storms brought ample snowfall in the mountains, the reservoirs would not fill. Twin Falls Canal Company had come to rely on those reservoirs to fill what once was a natural flow right from the river. Without the stored water, the company would run short in the coming season.

A water battle loomed.

The canal company has long blamed increased groundwater pumping in the Eastern Snake River Plain Aquifer in part for the decreased natural flow of the Snake River. A three-year old agreement, signed in 2001, had forestalled a showdown between groundwater pumpers with junior water rights and surface water users. But hopes that the temporary agreement could be negotiated into a long-term solution evaporated when it expired for a second time without a replacement in December 2004.

With the gloomy water outlook and the expired mitigation agreement, the canal company and six other irrigation companies that get their water from the Snake River or springs that depend on the aquifer took the action they long had threatened. On January 14, 2005, they handed a formal call for water to Karl Dreher, director of the Idaho Department of Water Resources. The coalition of seven surface water users asked him to deliver water "according to their senior natural flow and storage water rights" under state law, demanding the state uphold the prior appropriation doctrine.

Under the law, such a call required action by state officials. And action could require shutting down junior water rights, pitting thousands of people who depend on the water pumped from the ground against the thousands who depend on surface flows fed in part by groundwater. A lot was at stake, including perhaps, Dreher's job. The future of irrigated agriculture and the economy of southern Idaho depended on how the state and water users resolved the issue.

Groundwater users were understandably reluctant to give up their water without a fight. They challenged senior water users to prove they were injured and questioned whether shutting off the pumpers would even ensure water for the senior rights.

The call rekindled smoldering resentment dating to the early years of the twentieth century, when water users in the upper Snake River valley and the lower valley each suspected the other of withholding or falsely claiming water.

In 2001, Dreher had designated the American Falls Groundwater Management Area to control the declining aquifer level and dropping spring flows. The designation would have given Dreher greater authority to order immediate shut-offs. Before it went into effect, however, ground and surface water users signed a three-year mitigation agreement that forestalled Dreher's more onerous designation. But it didn't help.

"The conditions of the (aquifer) have not improved since 2001; in fact, aquifer levels and water supplies in the American Falls reach have only diminished," the coalition's January 14 letter said.

The groundwater pumpers fought back every step of the way. The pumpers, who together hold rights to irrigate about 855,000 acres, banded together in a group calling itself Idaho Ground Water Appropriators Inc. Most of them pump their water from the aquifer, and most have rights junior to the canal company and the coalition. But many also use water from canal systems. Together they challenged the assertions of the canal company and the surface water coalition, noting that the water rights at issue had not yet been adjudicated by the ongoing Snake River Basin Adjudication. They wanted to know how much a water shortage, should it happen, would actually harm the petitioners' senior rights. Does injury happen when water is available to raise adequate crops? How much has the petitioners' own use and renting of stored water affected the availability of water this year? Would shutting down groundwater pumpers simply contribute to water spilling past Milner Dam for hydropower generation? How much would be water rights that pumpers say were subordinated by the 1984 Swan Falls agreement (see Chapter 13), and how much would be used outside the state, such as for salmon migration?

They cited the state law that calls for "full economic development of underground water resources" and the state Constitution. They asked whether senior right holders can be liable for harm to junior rights for a call based on speculation, harassment or intimidation. And they were concerned about how designating the aquifer a groundwater management area would affect their ability to pump. They also questioned whether a call or curtailment of junior rights was justified when the senior water users had rights to enough stored water to meet their needs.

The pumpers also cited a 1912 U.S. Supreme Court ruling in the very first challenge to the Twin Falls Canal Company's water right by Henry Schodde (see Chapter Twelve). The canal company won that fight, but the pumpers tried to turn that historic victory against the surface water users. The judges in Schodde's day had noted that prior appropriation doctrine came with conditions. Their decision underscored a basic tenet in Idaho water law, that prior appropriation should not be used to block the fullest, most efficient development of the state's water resources. The groundwater pumpers argued that, like Schodde, the canal company and the surface water coalition had a right to a certain amount of water but not to a particular method of diversion. They argued that senior rights are not absolute but must account also for the needs of other users.

The trouble with the groundwater pumpers' comparison, canal company lawyer John Rosholt said, is that Schodde still had a right to all the water he needed, he just had to find a different way to get it to his fields. The pumpers were not arguing about the method of diversion, but about the amount of water. The surface water users are being denied access to water to which they are entitled because it is being intercepted by pumpers, he said. Other factors may be contributing, but increased groundwater pumping has made the conditions worse. Rosholt argued that efficient development should not be used to overrule other, older water rights.

Idaho Power, which runs seventeen hydroelectric plants on the Snake River, also has a lot at stake and weighed in on the canal company's side. "The eastern Snake River Plain Aquifer and the Snake River are over-appropriated, and depletions by groundwater users in the (aquifer) have caused declines in spring flows and reach gains tributary to the Snake River," the utility said in its February 14, 2005, petition to intervene in the call by the surface water coalition.

Idaho Power noted that its own water rights had been diminished as a result of groundwater pumping from the aquifer and the failure of the state to administer junior rights consistent with the state's prior appropriation doctrine. The company, fearing its water rights, and thus its ability to generate and sell power, would be further eroded, urged the state to resolve the issues raised by the canal company's call.

The state has acknowledged since the early 1980s that groundwater pumping affects the flow of springs that feed the Snake River. The Swan Falls case, involving Idaho Power water rights, in the early 1980s and the Musser case in the early 1990s, forced the state to recognize the connection and to develop rules to manage the two sources together. In both cases the state resisted the idea of curtailing junior water rights to protect senior rights. Officials argued unconvincingly that upholding Idaho Power's senior water right would interfere with future development, and they could take no action, because they had no rules yet to manage the sources together.

The surface water users' January 2005 call forced the issue.

In response, Dreher, understandably reluctant to shut down any water users, worked out a settlement that would allow most water users to continue to operate, offering some compensation or mitigation to senior water rights along with a program that included aquifer recharge. He proposed to cut back groundwater demand by having some pumpers convert to surface water, idling land under federal subsidy, and improving irrigation efficiency. State officials estimated that buying rights could save 150,000 to 200,000 acre-feet. The state has since bought out the water rights for the Bell Rapids project, on the bluffs above the Snake River west of Twin Falls, leaving 220,000 to 280,000 acre-feet in the river. That water will replace water now released from federal reservoirs upstream to help flush endangered salmon.

But skeptics and critics said Dreher's proposal was too complex and too expensive. It would cost the state an estimated $80 million to $130 million. They suggested that instead that the state should let the prior appropriation doctrine sort out the winners and losers. They also suggested marginal agricultural lands irrigated with groundwater should be dried up before the state and water users began shelling out millions of dollars for mitigation and compensation plans that might not work. They wanted the state to enforce existing water law that prohibits irrigating more land than a water right allows. And critics said Idaho Power should stop subsidizing irrigators, by making pumpers pay full price for the electricity they use to run their pumps. Others suggested expanding the state's water banks to encourage an open water market.

On May 2, 2005, in an amended order, Dreher predicted the Twin Falls Canal Company, which uses an average 1.1 million acre-feet per year, would run out of water during the 2005 season. He cited data from the Bureau of Reclamation showing a 30-percent reduction in the amount of water feeding the river in the American Falls reach, or a reduction of about 600,000 acre-feet per year. And the state's own recalibrated groundwater model "demonstrates that pumping under junior groundwater rights results in an approximate steady state annual depletion of 1.1 million acre-feet to the Snake River in the American Falls reach," he wrote.

Dreher ordered water users in districts where pumping directly affects spring flows, with priority dates of February 27, 1979, and later, to provide at least 27,000 acre-feet of replacement water in 2005 as mitigation to surface water users. Domestic in-home uses were not included. The order would have affected irrigation on about eighty thousand acres. It brought fears of widespread economic disruption, with impacts far beyond the 80,000 acres. But it never came to that.

As often happens in southern Idaho, serious discussion of drought and water supply forecasts are accompanied soon after, if not immediately, by heavy rain. The spring of 2005 was no different. In April, after the canal company and the coalition of surface water irrigators filed their call, the skies opened and dropped about four inches of rain. The rain brought some immediate relief, if not hope.

Then in June 2006, Fifth District Court Judge Barry Wood threw out Dreher's conjunctive management rules as unconstitutional because they ignored Idaho's prior appropriation doctrine and did not protect senior water rights. But Wood's decision was appealed, and in March 2007 it was overturned by the Idaho Supreme Court.

Water users on all sides of the issue make compelling arguments as to why they should be allowed to keep getting their full amount of water. The reality is that the water supply is finite, and there simply isn't enough to meet the growing demand. Across the arid West, large urban areas, such as Los Angeles and Las Vegas, demand more water and have the money and political power to get it. That doesn't bode well for the future of irrigated agriculture in southern Idaho and elsewhere. Increased efficiency no doubt can stretch the supply to meet more needs, but it cannot create more water. Cooperative efforts at long-term solutions will only go so far. The pie can only be split so many ways before the shares become meaningless.

Before that happens, John Rosholt and the canal company hope for a state water management plan that will ensure the long-term health of the aquifer and respect prior appropriation—a plan that will ensure cool, clean water for trout farms, ample flows for power generation and canal systems, and enough for groundwater pumpers while still leaving the Snake a river.

But those hopes may go unfulfilled. In Idaho, as elsewhere in the arid West, water fights likely will go on as long as there is any water left to fight over.

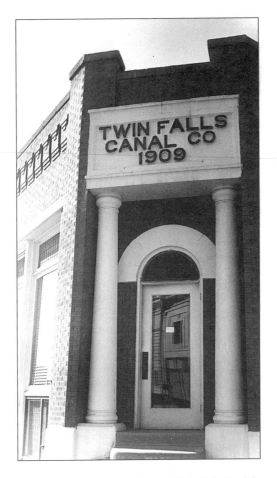

Courtesy Twin Falls Canal Co.

Sources:

Books:

Alt, David D. and Hyndman, Donald W. *Roadside Geology of Idaho.* Missoula: Mountain Press Publishing Co., 1989.

Arrington, Leonard J. *History of Idaho.* Moscow, Idaho: University of Idaho Press, 1994.

Barker, Rocky. *Saving all the Parts: Reconciling Economics and the Endangered Species Act.* Washington D.C. and Covelo, Calif.: Island Press, 1993.

Beal, Merrill D. and Wells, Merle. *History of Idaho.* New York: Lewis Historical Publishing Co. Inc., 1959.

Coleman, Edward Pierce. *Steel Rails and Territorial Tales.* Boise, Idaho: Limberlost Press, 1994.

Crawford, Stanley. *Mayor Domo: Chronicles of an Acequia in Northern New Mexico.* Albuquerque: University of New Mexico Press, 1988.

Dee, Lawrence. *The Geologic History of the Snake River Canyon at Twin Falls.* Boise, Idaho: Idaho Geological Survey, 1994.

Derig, Betty. *Roadside History of Idaho.* Missoula: Mountain Press Publishing Co., 1996.

Fiege, Mark. *Irrigated Eden: The Making of an Agricultural Landscape in the American West.* Seattle and London: University of Washington Press, 1999.

Fremont, John C. *The Exploring Expedition to the Rocky Mountains.* Washington D.C., London: Smithsonian Institution Press, 1988.

Hailey, John. *History of Idaho.* Boise, Idaho: Synes-York Company Inc., 1910.

Maley, Terry. *Exploring Idaho Geology.* Mineral Lands Publications, 1987.

Marston, Ed, editor. *Western Water Made Simple.* Covelo, Calif.: Island Press, 1987.

Moon, J. Howard. *A History of the Twin Falls Canal Company.* (N.p., July 1985.)

Palmer, Tim. *Snake River: A Window to the West.* Washington D.C. and Covelo, Calif.: Island Press, 1991.

Reisner, Marc. *Cadillac Desert: The American West and Its Disappearing Water.* New York: Viking, 1986.

Reisner, Marc and Bates, Sarah. *Overtapped Oasis: Reform or Revolution for Western Water.* Washington D.C. and Covelo, Calif.: Island Press, 1990.

Ricketts, Virginia. *A History of the Middle Snake River.* (N.p., n.d.).

Rogers, Peter. *America's Water: Federal Roles and Responsibilities.* Cambridge and London: MIT Press, 1996.

Shanks, Bernard. *This Land is Your Land: The Struggle to Save America's Public Lands.* San Francisco: Sierra Club Books, 1984.

Stuart, Robert. *The Discovery of the Oregon Trail.* Edited by Phillip Ashton Rollings. (1935; reprint, Lincoln and London: University of Nebraska Press, 1995).

Walgamott, Charles S. *Six Decades Back.* Caldwell, Idaho: Caxton Printers Ltd., 1936.

Wittfogel, Karl. *Oriental Despotism: A Comparative Study of Total Power.* New Haven: Yale University, 1957.

Worster, Donald. *Rivers of Empire: Water, Aridity and the Growth of the American West.* New York and Oxford: Oxford University Press, 1985.

—. *A River Running West: The Life of John Wesley Powell.* New York and Oxford: Oxford University Press, 2001.

Periodicals:

Fereday, Jeffrey C. and Creamer, Michael C. "Swan Falls in 3-D: A new look at the historical, legal and practical dimensions of Idaho's biggest water rights controversy." *Idaho Law Review,* 1991-1992, Volume 28, No. 3, p. 573-643.

Frederick, Kenneth D. "Water Marketing: Obstacles and Opportunities." *Forum for Applied Research and Public Policy,* Spring 2001.

Gease, Deryl V. "William N. Byers and the Case for Federal Air to Irrigation in the Arid West." *Colorado Magazine,* Vol. 45, No. 4, Fall 1968, p. 340-345.

Gentry, James R. "Euro-American Encounters with the Twin Falls Area 1864-1868." *Idaho Yesterdays,* Vol. 38, No. 4, Winter 1995, p. 12-19.

Lovins, Hugh. "Carey Act Failures." *Idaho Yesterdays,* Vol. 30 No. 3, Fall 1986, p. 9-24.

—. "The Carey Act in Idaho, 1895-1925." *Pacific Northwest Quarterly,* Vol. 78, No. 4, October 1987.

Jackson, W. Turrentine. "Wells Fargo and Co. in Idaho Territory: the 1870s and Beyond." *Idaho Yesterdays,* Vol. 27, No. 1, Spring 1983.

Neil, J. Meredith. "A Forgotten Alternative." *Idaho Yesterdays,* Vol. 9, No. 4, Winter 1965-66, p. 18-22.

Rosholt, John. "Irrigation and Politics." *Idaho Yesterdays,* Spring/Summer 1986, Volume 30, No. 1-2, p.20-25.

Newspapers:

Brock, William. "Canal 'break' leads to water spill." *Twin Falls (Idaho) Times-News,* 23 May 1995.

—. "Abyss Amiss: Giant Sinkhole Opens Beneath Canal." *Twin Falls Times-News,* 12 November 1996.

—. "In a high-tech world, there's still room for a canal company trapper." *Twin Falls Times-News,* 19 April 1997.

—. "Workers plug dam leak. Hole at Milner never threatened canal system." *Twin Falls Times-News,* 28 September 1998.

Snyder, Cindy. "Vince Alberdi lives, breathes irrigation." *Twin Falls (Idaho) Ag Weekly,* 23 October 1998.

"Place a valuation wanted by Hollister." *Shoshone (Idaho) Journal,* Vol. 19, No. 14, 18 April 1902.

"Court in Session: The Hollister-Clark Case Goes to Federal Court." *Shoshone Journal,* Vol. 19, No. 15, 25 April 1902.

"The Twin Falls Land and Power Company will expend $1,500,000." *Shoshone Journal,* Vol. 19, No. 16, 2 May 1902.

"Court proceedings: Case of Hollister against state now on trial." *Shoshone Journal,* Vol. 19, No. 17, 9 May 1902.

"Jury gives $1,000 damages to defendants." *Shoshone Journal,* Vol. 19, No. 18, 16 May 1902.

"Our analysis of the aquifer issue." *The Boise (Idaho) Statesman,* 16 January 2005.

Other sources:

"The Snake River Canal, Idaho." *Engineering News,* Vol. 18, 17 December 1887, p. 444.

Williams, Hon. Mikel H. "The History and Development and Current Status of the Carey Act in Idaho." Boise, Idaho: Idaho Department of Reclamation, March 1970.

U.S. House Committee on Energy and Commerce. *Swan Falls Agreement.* 100th Cong., 1st Sess. November 1987. Report 100-148.

Chapman, Sherl L. "Irrigated Agriculture: Idaho's Economic Lifeblood." Idaho Water Users Association, Boise, Idaho, photocopy (n.d.).

Rosholt, John A. "The dichotomy of it all." Presented at the Snake River Symposium, Twin Falls, Idaho, 21 October 1982.

Index

About the Author:

Photo by Eric Stansbury

Niels Sparre Nokkentved lives with his wife in Boise, Idaho. His writing and reporting have earned him several awards for investigative journalism. Born in Denmark, he grew up in western Canada and northern Illinois. The Vietnam War and the U.S. Navy brought him to California in 1968. After the service he traveled extensively before moving to Washington to attend college. He earned degrees in journalism and environmental studies from Western Washington University. Since 1986 he has written about natural resource issues for newspapers in Idaho, Washington and Utah. This is his second book.